Edited by I. A. HOROWITZ

Galahad Books • New York City

PLAY CHESS with the masters and grand masters. Whenever and wherever you wish. Profit from their good moves; and, because they are fallible like yourself, learn how to avoid the mistakes they made.

When you're avid for a game and can't find a partner, this book, *Solitaire Chess*, will provide you with 62 different opponents, the foremost virtuosos of the royal game from the current, modern, hypermodern, romantic and classical eras of chess.

You play 62 different games with the White pieces, and you see move-by-move how your play compares with the moves actually made in the historical games presented herewith.

Here is how you play SOLITAIRE CHESS:

First Step: Play the actual moves given in the preamble text printed on the top of each right-hand page of the book (each game is an actual game played in master-tourney competition).

Second Step: Cover up (with blotter, paper or anything handy) all the succeeding moves (given in the column text).

Third Step: Uncover just Black's next move, and play it.

Fourth Step: Now *guess* White's next move.

Fifth Step: Then uncover just one pair of moves, the move you may have guessed and Black's reply; and compare your guess with White's actual move, and make Black's actual reply. If your White guess is correct, score yourself Par (the Par score is given alongside the move). If your White guess is incorrect, score yourself zero.

Remaining Step: Then continue, uncovering one move at a time, until completion of game.

Final Step: Now total your score and see how you rate.

In this manner, the following pages will supply you with 62 chess partners (all different, all famous); will combine entertainment with instruction and furnish a testing method to rate your chess knowledge and talent.

The game examples were chosen from the pages of *Chess Review,* in which SOLITAIRE CHESS has been for many years a most popular feature.

This is a self-sufficient and satisfying book for all chess-players. Using it, the beginner will rapidly become a good, better-than-average practitioner, the average player will become an expert.

In addition, there are informative comments on each page following the given game. They deal variously with chess strategy and tactics and opening, middle- and end-game objectives. Often they explain how the gain or loss of time, space or material affect the outcome of the game. And they discuss relevant points on attack, counter-attack, defense and sacrificial combinations.

I. A. HOROWITZ

ALEKHINE'S LEGACY

Alekhine's name will always excite a terrifying awe even in the giants of chessdom. From first to last, his play was stirring and precise. Just before his demise, he takes young Pomar (Black) at Gijon, 1945. The opening, a Catalan begins with 1 P–Q4, P–Q4 2 P–QB4, P–K3 3 N–KB3, N–KB3 4 P–KN3, B–K2 5 B–N2, O–O 6 O–O, P–B3 7 QN–Q2, QN–Q2 8 Q–B2, R–K1 9 R–Q1, Q–B2 10 P–N3, PxP (a) 11 NxP.

Cover scoring table at line indicated. Set up position, make Black's next move (exposing table just enough to read it). Now guess White's 12th move, then expose it. Score par, if move agrees; zero, if not. Make move actually given, Black's reply. Then *guess* White's next, and so on.

COVER WHITE MOVES
IN TABLE BELOW.   EXPOSE ONE LINE AT A TIME

White Played	Par Score	Black Played		Your Selection for White's move	Your Score
		11 . . . . N–B1		. . . .	. . . .
12 B–B4	3	12 . . . . Q–Q1		. . . .	. . . .
13 P–K4	3	13 . . . . N–N3		. . . .	. . . .
14 B–N5	5	14 . . . . P–KR3	(b)	. . . .	. . . .
15 B–K3	3	15 . . . . Q–B2		. . . .	. . . .
16 KN–K5 . . .	5	16 . . . . NxN		. . . .	. . . .
17 PxN	3	17 . . . . N–Q2		. . . .	. . . .
18 P–B4	4	18 . . . . N–N3		. . . .	. . . .
19 N–Q6	4	19 . . . . R–Q1		. . . .	. . . .
20 N–N5	5	20 . . . . Q–N1		. . . .	. . . .
21 RxR†	3	21 . . . . BxR		. . . .	. . . .
22 N–Q6	3	22 . . . . Q–B2		. . . .	. . . .
23 P–QR4 . . .	4	23 . . . . B–K2		. . . .	. . . .
24 R–Q1	3	24 . . . . N–Q2		. . . .	. . . .
25 P–QN4 . . .	3	25 . . . . P–QN3		. . . .	. . . .
26 Q–Q2	3	26 . . . . N–B1		. . . .	. . . .
27 P–B5	4	27 . . . . P–B3	(c)	. . . .	. . . .
28 PxBP	3	28 . . . . BxP		. . . .	. . . .
29 N–K8!	4	29 . . . . Q–K2		. . . .	. . . .
30 NxB†	3	30 . . . . QxN*		. . . .	. . . .
31 P–K5 (d) .	6	31 . . . . Q–B2	(e)	. . . .	. . . .
32 P–B6	5	32 . . . . B–N2		. . . .	. . . .
33 PxP	2	33 . . . . QxP		. . . .	. . . .
34 P–N5	2	34 . . . . PxP		. . . .	. . . .
35 BxRP	2	35 . . . . Q–R2		. . . .	. . . .
36 Q–N5†	3	36 . . . . K–R1		. . . .	. . . .
37 Q–B6†	2	37 . . . . K–N1		. . . .	. . . .
38 BxB	3	38 . . . . QxKB		. . . .	. . . .
39 R–Q4	4	39 . . . . K–R2		. . . .	. . . .
40 BxN	2	40 . . . . Resigns		. . . .	. . . .

Total Score 100 | Your Percentage . . . .

SCALE: 75-100—Excellent; 55-74—Superior; 40-54—Good; 25-39—Fair

Notes on ALEKHINE vs. POMAR

Goliath defeats young David, for at the time of this contest Pomar was a boy prodigy, and the first player from Spain since the days of Lopez to put his country on the chess map.

Lopez was a Spanish priest who wrote about chess in 1590, advocating and playing the opening named after him: "the Ruy Lopez." On the continent, this debut is called the Spanish Game.

The chess world had to wait almost 400 years before the Iberian Peninsula again figured in chess nomenclature. A decade ago, the players of Barcelona perfected a system in the Queen Pawn game, wherein the insertion of P–KN3 at the correct time gives a more elastic advantage to the White side than the original Reti system. This is the Catalan Opening, popular today.

The trouble with Pomar's Black game was that his routine was "too routine." After a Pawn sacrifice opens the way, White's lurking Bishops rake the enemy on both wings until the Black monarch perishes.

*Position after 30 . . . QxN

NOTES TO THE GAME

a) Now Black is doomed to passivity. Better is 10 . . . P–QN3 and . . . B–N2.

b) Because of this move, Black is compelled to exchange Knights on his 16th move and grant White the open Queen file. But there is hardly anything better.

c) On 27 . . . B–N2, White wins with 28 BxRP! PxB 29 QxP.

d) The point. White's Bishop comes alive.

e) On 31 . . . QxKP 32 BxBP wins a Rook, or 31 . . . QxBP 32 BxBP, R–N1 33 R–KB1, QxP 34 RxN†, KxR 35 Q–Q8†, K–B2 36 B–K8†, and White mates.

6

FINE FETTLE

A little over a decade ago, the American scene was almost topheavy with great players, many of whom have gone into retirement. Reuben Fine was one of them. Here we see him as White, in Fine fettle, demolish the French Defense of Flohr at AVRO, 1938, all because of one infinitesimal inaccuracy. The game begins with 1 P–K4, P–K3 2 P–Q4, P–Q4 3 N–QB3, B–N5 4 P–K5.

Cover scoring table at line indicated. Set up position, make Black's next move (exposing table just enough to read it). Now guess White's 5th move, then expose it. Score par, if move agrees; zero, if not. Make move actually given, Black's reply. Then guess White's next, and so on.

COVER WHITE MOVES
IN TABLE BELOW.   EXPOSE ONE LINE AT A TIME

White Played	Par Score	Black Played	Your Selection for White's move	Your Score
		4 .... P–QB4	....	....
5 B–Q2	 3	5 .... N–K2	....	....
6 N–B3	 3	6 .... N–B4? (a)	....	....
7 PxP	 4	7 .... BxP	....	....
8 B–Q3	 3	8 .... N–R5	....	....
9 O–O	 3	9 .... N–B3	....	....
10 R–K1	 3	10 .... P–KR3	....	....
11 N–R4! (b)	6	11 .... B–B1	....	....
12 R–QB1	 4	12 .... B–Q2	....	....
13 NxN	 3	13 .... QxN	....	....
14 P–QB4!	... 5	14 .... PxP	....	....
15 RxP	 4	15 .... Q–Q1	....	....
16 Q–R5	 5	16 .... N–K2	....	....
17 R–Q4	 4	17 .... P–KN3	....	....
18 Q–B3	 3	18 .... Q–B2	....	....
19 N–B3	 3	19 .... N–B4	....	....
20 N–N5	 5	20 .... Q–N3 *	....	....
21 RxB (c)	... 7	21 .... KxR	....	....
22 P–KN4	 5	22 .... N–R5	....	....
23 QxBP†	 4	23 .... B–K2	....	....
24 B–N4	 4	24 .... QR–K1	....	....
25 BxB	 4	25 .... RxB	....	....
26 Q–B6	 5	26 .... P–R3	....	....
27 R–Q1	 5	27 .... PxN	....	....
28 B–K4§ (d)	5	28 .... Resigns	....	....

Total Score 100 | Your Percentage ----------------------

SCALE: 75-100—Excellent; 55-74—Superior; 40-54—Good; 25-39—Fair

Notes on FINE vs. FLOHR

Black's 11 . . . B–B1 is an inaccuracy from which he cannot recover. The delay in castling allows White to execute threats on both flanks. The overly careful retention, on Black's part, of a two-Bishop setup at the cost of development is properly punished.

Kashdan and Janowski were also known as "Bishop lovers." Parodying one of Harry Lauder's songs, the Polish master averred: "I'd rather lose my Queen than lose my Bishop!"

En passant, one of the main points in estimating end-game chances, where only minor pieces and pawns are on the board, is the correct appraisal of the long-range efficiency of Bishop vs. Knight—and vice versa. There is no general rule which should be preferred. Each position has its delicate balances and counters.

Particularly to be avoided, however, is the "bad" Bishop plus Rook Pawn setup vs. lone King, where the Pawn cannot be queened because the promotion square is not commanded by the "right-colored" Bishop.

NOTES TO THE GAME

a) Correct is 6 . . . QN-B3 or 6 . . . O-O.

b) White prepares for Queen-side activity while gaining a Bishop for a Knight or driving the Bishop to an awkward post.

c) The denouement.

d) Black loses material or gets mated.

*Diagram shows the position after 20 . . . Q–N3.

---

† = check;   ‡ = double check;   § = dis. check

8

KEEPING THE WOLF FROM THE DOOR

WHEN Pillsbury (White) met Wolf, he kept him from the door by no niggardly means but rather by expending a piece. And it happened appropriately enough at Monte Carlo (1902). The Opening is a Queen's Indian Defense: 1 P-Q4, N-KB3 2 P-QB4, P-K3 3 N-QB3, P-QN3 4 P-K4! B-N2 5 B-Q3, P-Q4 6 BPxP, PxP 7 P-K5, N-K5 8 N-B3.

Cover scoring table at line indicated. Set up position, make Black's next move (exposing table just enough to read it). Now guess White's 8th move, then expose it. Score par if your move agrees; zero, if not. Make move actually given, opponent's reply. Then guess White's next and so on.

COVER WHITE MOVES

IN TABLE BELOW.   EXPOSE ONE LINE AT A TIME

White Played	Par Score	Black Played	Your Selection for White's move	Your Score
		8 . . . . B-K2 (a)	------------------	--------
9 O-O _____ 2		9 . . . . O-O? (b)	------------------	--------
10 Q-B2 _____ 4		10 . . . . NxN (c)	------------------	--------
11 BxP† _____ 6		11 . . . . K-R1	------------------	--------
12 PxN _____ 4		12 . . . . P-N3*	------------------	--------
13 BxP! (d) _ 7		13 . . . . PxB	------------------	--------
14 QxP _____ 2		14 . . . . Q-K1	------------------	--------
15 Q-R6† ____ 3		15 . . . . K-N1	------------------	--------
16 N-N5 _____ 5		16 . . . . BxN	------------------	--------
17 QxB† _____ 3		17 . . . . K-B2 (e)	------------------	--------
18 P-KB4 ____ 4		18 . . . . K-K3	------------------	--------
19 P-B5† ____ 3		19 . . . . K-Q2	------------------	--------
20 Q-N7† ____ 6		20 . . . . K-B1 (f)	------------------	--------
21 P-K6 _____ 3		21 . . . . R-N1	------------------	--------
22 Q-R7 _____ 3		22 . . . . R-R1	------------------	--------
23 Q-N6 _____ 3		23 . . . . B-R3	------------------	--------
24 QxQ† _____ 3		24 . . . . RxQ	------------------	--------
25 R-K1 _____ 3		25 . . . . N-B3	------------------	--------
26 B-N5 _____ 5		26 . . . . N-Q1	------------------	--------
27 BxN _____ 3		27 . . . . KxB	------------------	--------
28 P-B6 _____ 3		28 . . . . R-R1	------------------	--------
29 R-K5 _____ 5		29 . . . . P-B3	------------------	--------
30 QR-K1 ___ 3		30 . . . . R-QB1	------------------	--------
31 R-N5 _____ 5		31 . . . . B-Q6	------------------	--------
32 R/1-K5 ___ 5		32 . . . . R-R3	------------------	--------
33 R-N8† ____ 7		and White won	------------------	--------

| Total Score 100 | Your Percentage ------------------- | ------- |

SCALE: 75-100—Excellent; 55-74—Superior; 40-54—Good; 25-39—Fair

Notes on PILLSBURY vs. WOLF

Four connected passed Pawns and the initiative are worth much more than a piece. A sacrifice of this sort does not have to be analyzed exhaustively, fearing the consequences of the countless variations which may develop from the offer. The sacrifice is based on general principles. White should secure the winning end-game possibility by forcing as soon as possible an exchange of Queens.

When Pillsbury was twenty-three he captured first prize in the famous Hastings Tournament of 1895, ahead of the greatest masters of the day: Tchigorin, Lasker, Tarrasch, Steinitz, among others. This, his first international success, was his greatest.

In his last years, Pillsbury's play was handicapped by an incurable illness to which he succumbed at the age of thirty-four.

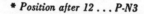

Position after 12 ... P-N3

NOTES TO THE GAME

a) Not 8 . . . B-N5 for then White wins a piece with 9 Q-R4†, N-B3 10 B-QN5, BxN† 11 PxB, Q-Q2 12 P-K6! PxP 13 N-K5, NxQBP 14 Q-B2.

b) Better is 9 . . . P-KB4 at once.

c) Now 10 . . . P-KB4 is met by 11 PxP e.p. NxP/3 12 N-N5.

d) Lengthily calculated and to a King hunt not in itself decisive but leading to a winning end-game all the while a piece down.

e) 17 . . . K-R2 brings the same response.

f) Or 20 . . . Q-K2 21 P-K6†, K-K1 22 Q-N6†, K-Q1 23 B-N5.

10

"AND EVEN HOMER NODS"

Very few grandmasters could boast of a positional victory over the "invincible" Capablanca. But here—and it's no April Fool joke—is just such a victory. At New York 1924 and in a Reti Opening, Reti (White —what else?) teaches the World Champion some of the finer points of this esoteric debut. The introductory moves are 1 N–KB3, N–KB3 2 P–B4, P–KN3 3 P–QN4, B–N2 4 B–N2, O–O 5 P–N3, P–N3 6 B–N2.

Cover scoring table at line indicated. Set up position, make Black's next move (exposing table just enough to read it). Now *guess* White's 7th move, then expose it. Score par, if move agrees; zero, if not. Make move actually given, Black's reply. Then guess White's next, and so on.

COVER WHITE MOVES
IN TABLE BELOW.   EXPOSE ONE LINE AT A TIME

White Played	Par Score	Black Played	Your Selection for White's move	Your Score
		6 . . . . B–N2	. . . .	. . . .
7 O–O 3		7 . . . . P–Q3	. . . .	. . . .
8 P–Q3 3		8 . . . . QN–Q2	. . . .	. . . .
9 QN–Q2 3		9 . . . . P–K4	. . . .	. . . .
10 Q–B2 3		10 . . . . R–K1	. . . .	. . . .
11 KR–Q1 4		11 . . . . P–QR4	. . . .	. . . .
12 P–QR3 4		12 . . . . P–R3 (a)	. . . .	. . . .
13 N–B1 4		13 . . . . P–B4	. . . .	. . . .
14 P–N5 4		14 . . . . N–B1	. . . .	. . . .
15 P–K3 4		15 . . . . Q–B2	. . . .	. . . .
16 P–Q4 4		16 . . . . B–K5	. . . .	. . . .
17 Q–B3 3		17 . . . . KPxP	. . . .	. . . .
18 PxP 3		18 . . . . N/3–Q2 (b)	. . . .	. . . .
19 Q–Q2 5		19 . . . . PxP (c)	. . . .	. . . .
20 BxP 5		20 . . . . QxP	. . . .	. . . .
21 BxB 4		21 . . . . KxB	. . . .	. . . .
22 Q–N2† 4		22 . . . . K–N1	. . . .	. . . .
23 RxP 4		23 . . . . Q–B4	. . . .	. . . .
24 QR–Q1 4		24 . . . . R–R2	. . . .	. . . .
25 N–K3 4		25 . . . . Q–R4 (d)	. . . .	. . . .
26 N–Q4 5		26 . . . . BxB	. . . .	. . . .
27 KxB 4		27 . . . . Q–K4	. . . .	. . . .
28 N–B4 5		28 . . . . Q–QB4	. . . .	. . . .
29 N–B6 5		29 . . . . R–B2	. . . .	. . . .
30 N–K3 4		30 . . . . N–K4	. . . .	. . . .
31 R/1–Q5 5		31 . . . . Resigns(e)*	. . . .	. . . .
Total Score 100		Your Percentage	

SCALE: 75-100—Excellent; 55-74—Superior; 40-54—Good; 25-39—Fair

Notes on RETI vs. CAPABLANCA

This defeat of the Cuban genius, his first setback at the end of a ten-year span without any losses, came at a very inauspicious time in the fifth round of the great New York Tournament, 1924.

Capablanca had completed four games, all draws, proving his statement: "I can draw at will against any master." It gave him a very indifferent score, indeed, in a tourney which included such renowned fighters as Emanuel Lasker, Marshall, Alekhine, and the lion-killer, Reti.

Now, after Reti's victory, Capablanca stood 2 and 3. He made an amazing comeback; from then on in he did not lose a game outright, nor was he ever seriously endangered. He finished 14½ and 5½, in second place behind Lasker.

For too long had chessdom's sharpshooters hoped to topple the invincible Cuban. His icy perfection, his ability to squeeze victory from a pin-point edge, had baffled and frustrated them. Finally, it was a newcomer, Richard Reti, an advocate of a strange style, sharp and perverse, who brought down the world champion.

"Hypermoderns," the followers of Reti called themselves.

Final Position

NOTES TO THE GAME

a) The opening has been treated well by Black who has achieved equality.

b) 18 . . . N–K3 is correct as may be seen in 19 PxP, QPxP 20 Q–B1 etc.

c) Here 19 . . . QR–Q1 is better.

d) Now White's men are in commanding positions in the center.

e) If 31 . . . N–B5, White wins at least the Exchange: 32 RxQ, NxQ 33 R–B2, N–R5 34 N–Q5.

† = check; ‡ = double check; § = dis. check

MAXIMS ARE FOR THE BIRDS

There are two sides to every maxim. "Castle early," for example, to unite the Rooks eventually on the first rank. But castling also apprises the enemy of the site of your King. Here, in one of the games of the match between Steinitz and Tchigorin, world champion Steinitz (White) briskly utilizes this information. The opening, a Ruy Lopez, begins the hostilities with 1 P-K4, P-K4 2 N-KB3, N-QB3 3 B-N5, N-B3 4 P-Q3(a).

Cover scoring table at line indicated. Set up position, make Black's next move (exposing table just enough to read it). Now guess White's 5th move, then expose it. Score par, if move agrees; zero, if not. Make move actually given, Black's reply. Then guess White's next, and so on.

**COVER WHITE MOVES
IN TABLE BELOW.**

EXPOSE ONE LINE AT A TIME

White Played	Par Score	Black Played	Your Selection for White's move	Your Score
		4 . . . . P-Q3	. . . .	. . . .
5 P-B3 3		5 . . . . P-KN3	. . . .	. . . .
6 QN-Q2 3		6 . . . . B-N2	. . . .	. . . .
7 N-B1 3		7 . . . . O-O	. . . .	. . . .
8 B-QR4 2		8 . . . . N-Q2	. . . .	. . . .
9 N-K3 3		9 . . . . N-B4	. . . .	. . . .
10 B-B2 3		10 . . . N-K3	. . . .	. . . .
11 P-KR4 (b) . 5		11 . . . N-K2	. . . .	. . . .
12 P-R5 5		12 . . . P-Q4	. . . .	. . . .
13 RPxP 4		13 . . . . BPxP (c)	. . . .	. . . .
14 PxP 4		14 . . . . NxP	. . . .	. . . .
15 NxN 3		15 . . . . QxN	. . . .	. . . .
16 B-N3 4		16 . . . . Q-B3	. . . .	. . . .
17 Q-K2 3		17 . . . . B-Q2	. . . .	. . . .
18 B-K3 3		18 . . . . K-R1	. . . .	. . . .
19 O-O-O 3		19 . . . . QR-K1	. . . .	. . . .
20 Q-B1 (d) . . 6		20 . . . . P-QR4	. . . .	. . . .
21 P-Q4 4		21 . . . . PxP	. . . .	. . . .
22 NxP 5		22 . . . . BxN	. . . .	. . . .
23 RxB (e) . . . 7		23 . . . . NxR*	. . . .	. . . .
24 RxP† 7		24 . . . . KxR	. . . .	. . . .
25 Q-R1† 4		25 . . . . K-N2	. . . .	. . . .
26 B-R6† 4		26 . . . . K-B3	. . . .	. . . .
27 Q-R4† 4		27 . . . . K-K4	. . . .	. . . .
28 QxN† 4		28 . . . . K-B4	. . . .	. . . .
29 Q-B4 mate 4				

Total Score 100 | **Your Percentage** _____ | _____

SCALE: 75-100—Excellent; 55-74—Superior; 40-54—Good; 25-39—Fair

Notes on STEINITZ vs. TCHIGORIN

Tchigorin had many original opening ideas. Many of them, after refinements, are current opening variations. In his heyday, though, Tchigorin was the lone exponent of the Tchigorin systems.

The present game is an example of a Tchigorin eccentricity in the opening. It should not be criticized per se. The Pawn setup would have been sufficient for defense had Black retained his King Bishop. Exchanging this piece was the fatal error, for it denuded the Black King.

Steinitz has left behind a reputation as a dour, attrition-edge player. This appraisal is not justified. He won many brilliancies, more than the majority of his peers. Why, then, his reputation as a tenacious defender, but without dash? Probably, because of his beard.

Notes to the Game

*Position is diagrammed after 23 ... NxR

a) A timid, some might say conservative, but solid beginning.

b) White is aiming his Rook where Black's King lives.

c) 13 ... RPxP is better.

d) This is not a defensive move at all. See White's 25th.

e) Initiating the end!

† = check; ‡ = double check; § = dis. check

TARRASCH THE TRENCHANT

THE ROMANTICISTS had a way. They could make a staid French Defense look like a combination of gambits rolled into one. Here grandmaster Tarrasch (White) shows the way: first game, 1916 match with Mieses (Mieses could dish it out; but could he take it?): 1 P-Q4, P-K3 2 P-K4, P-Q4 3 N-QB3, PxP 4 NxP, QN-Q2 5 N-KB3.

Cover scoring table at line indicated. Set up position, make Black's next move (exposing table just enough to read that move). Guess White's sixth move. Now expose next line; score par, if your move agrees; score zero, if not. Make move given, then guess White's next, and so on.

COVER WHITE MOVES
IN TABLE BELOW.   EXPOSE ONE LINE AT A TIME

White Played	Par Score.	Black Played	Your Selection for White's move	Your Score
		5 . . . . KN–B3	------------------	---------
6 B–Q3	4	6 . . . . NxN	------------------	---------
7 BxN	3	7 . . . . N–B3	------------------	---------
8 B–N5	4	8 . . . . B–K2	------------------	---------
9 BxN	6	9 . . . . PxB (a)	------------------	---------
10 Q–K2	4	10 . . . . P–B3	------------------	---------
11 O–O–O	5	11 . . . . Q–B2	------------------	---------
12 KR–K1	3	12 . . . . B–Q2	------------------	---------
13 K–N1	3	13 . . . . O–O–O	------------------	---------
14 P–B4	5	14 . . . . B–N5	------------------	---------
15 R–R1	3	15 . . . . B–Q3	------------------	---------
16 P–B5	4	16 . . . . B–B1	------------------	---------
17 Q–B4	3	17 . . . . B–N2	------------------	---------
18 Q–R4	3	18 . . . . K–N1	------------------	---------
19 B–B2	3	19 . . . . B–QB1	------------------	---------
20 R–Q3	4	20 . . . . R–Q2	------------------	---------
21 R–R3	4	21 . . . . P–QR3	------------------	---------
22 R–N3	4	22 . . . . K–R2	------------------	---------
23 R–N6	4	23 . . . . KR–Q1	------------------	---------
24 Q–R5	3	24 . . . . R–K2 (b)	------------------	---------
25 P–QN4	4	25 . . . . P–B4	------------------	---------
26 R–Q1	2	26 . . . . P–K4	------------------	---------
27 P–QR4	3	27 . . . . P–K5	------------------	---------
28 P–N5 (c) *	5	28 . . . . PxN? (d)	------------------	---------
29 RxRP†	4	29 . . . . PxR	------------------	---------
30 P–N6†	3	30 . . . . K–R1	------------------	---------
31 PxQ	1	31 . . . . R/1–Q2	------------------	---------
32 BxP	1	32 . . . . RxBP	------------------	---------
33 BxB	1	33 . . . . RxB	------------------	---------
34 QxP†	1	34 . . . . K–N1	------------------	---------
35 PxP	1	35 . . . . R–Q2	------------------	---------
36 K–B2	2	36 . . . . Resigns	------------------	---------

Total Score   100 | Your Percentage ------------------ | ---------

SCALE: 75-100—Excellent; 55-74—Superior; 40-54—Good; 25-39—Fair

15

Notes on TARRASCH vs. MIESES

Disregarding theoretical correctness of an attacking line, the attacker always possesses a psychological edge. In addition, it is the attacker who has the most fun. The harried defender is constantly under pressure.

Continuous pressure produces blunders. It follows then that defense must make more blunders than attack. This theory, however, has never been confirmed by statistical research into the games of the masters.

Contrary to popular opinion, it is the defender who must be the better tactician. Accepting the usual prefatory sacrifice of Pawn or piece, he must be able to refute more than one line of attack.

The defender must always keep in mind the old proverb: "There is more than one way to skin a cat." Or checkmate a King.

*Position after 28 P-N5

NOTES TO THE GAME

a) On 9 . . . BxB 10 Q-Q3 prevents Black's castling, threatens 11 BxNP and prepares castling long with good prospects.

b) Black aims for 25 . . . P-B4 and capture of the Queen Pawn (24 . . . P-B4 25 R-Q1. BxP? 26 NxB, RxN 27 RxRP†!!).

c) Finale of the Pawn demonstration. Implicit is a trap.

d) 28 . . . K-N1 is correct, whereafter the game should be a draw: 29 PxBP, PxN 30 PxP, BxP 31 P-B6, R-Q4!

Time pressure caused the blunder.

16

WHO IS THE POTTER, PRAY?

FRANK MARSHALL and RUDOLPH SPIELMANN, two of the greatest attacking players of all time, were contemporaries and contested many games with each other. In this encounter, it is Marshall who attacks: Spielmann is the Pot. The opening, a Staunton Gambit in the Dutch Defense, begins with 1 P-Q4, P-KB4 2 P-K4, PxP 3 N-QB3.

Cover the scoring table at the line indicated. Set up the position and make Black's next move (exposing the table just enough to read that move). Now guess White's next move, expose the next line. Score par if your move agrees; score zero if it does not. Make the move actually given and the opponent's reply. Then guess White's next move, and continue in similar fashion to the end of the game.

COVER WHITE MOVES
IN TABLE BELOW.   EXPOSE ONE LINE AT A TIME

White Played	Par Score	Black Played	Your Selection for White's move	Your Score
		3 . . . . N–KB3	-----------------	--------
4 B–N5	3	4 . . . . P–B3	-----------------	--------
5 P–B3!	8	5 . . . . PxP (a)	-----------------	--------
6 NxP	3	6 . . . . P–K3	-----------------	--------
7 B–Q3	4	7 . . . . B–K2	-----------------	--------
8 O–O	4	8 . . . . P–Q3	-----------------	--------
9 Q–K2	4	9 . . . . N–R3	-----------------	--------
10 P–QR3 (b)	5	10 . . . . N–B2	-----------------	--------
11 QR–K1	4	11 . . . . P–QN3	-----------------	--------
12 N–KR4	6	12 . . . . K–Q2 (c)	-----------------	--------
13 N–B5! (d)	10	13 . . . . Q–KB1	-----------------	--------
14 NxB	4	14 . . . . QxN	-----------------	--------
15 N–K4	3	15 . . . . R–B1	-----------------	--------
16 NxN†	4	16 . . . . PxN	-----------------	--------
17 Q–B3	5	17 . . . . N–K1 *	-----------------	--------
18 RxP!! (e)	2	18 . . . . Q–B2	-----------------	--------
19 R–K4!	8	19 . . . . B–N2	-----------------	--------
20 R–KR4	6	20 . . . . N–N2	-----------------	--------
21 RxP	2	21 . . . . R–R1	-----------------	--------
22 Q–R3†	6	. . . . Resigns	-----------------	--------
Total Score	100	Your Percentage -------------------		————

SCALE: 75-100—Excellent; 55-74—Superior; 40-54—Good; 25-39—Fair

17

Notes on MARSHALL vs. SPIELMANN

If Black wants to avoid the many pitfalls of the Staunton Gambit, but still have in mind playing a Dutch Defense, he must play after 1 P–Q4, 1 . . . P–K3. Then if 2 P–QB4, 2 . . . P–KB4. However, White may not accommodate Black, and can transfer the game into the French Defense by 2 P–K4.

Botvinnik, the world champion (at this writing) has gained many successes with the Dutch Defense. It is interesting that in his games with this debut against many grandmasters, not one of them had the temerity to essay the Staunton Gambit.

In the present game Marshall's sharp and precise thrusts against the awkward placement of the Black King and his congested entourage punishes his opponent for the mismanagement of the opening.

Position after 17 . . . N-K1

NOTES TO THE GAME

a) 5 . . . P-K6, returning the Pawn, is safer. Better development and control of the center compensate for White's Pawn minus.

b) To retain the King Bishop.

c) 13 BxN, BxB 14 Q-R5† forces . . . K-Q2, anyway.

d) Inviting 13 . . . PxN 14 BxP†, K-K1 15 BxB, RxB 16 RxN! PxR 17 BxP.

e) Note how busy this Rook becomes: 18 . . . KxR? 19 Q-B5†, K-B2 20 QxRP†, N-N2 21 B-N6†, K-K3 22 R-K1†, and White wins.

IS THIS THE SYSTEM?

THE QUEST for an ideal winning system has engaged the attention of all manner of chess-players from time out of mind. Systems come and systems go, but the Colle System goes on like Tennyson's brook. For example, at Hastings, 1928, Belgian master Edgard Colle, after whom the system is named, impresses his current adversary, Buerger, with its lethal effects. With a running start, can you pick the correct moves? The game begins with 1 P-Q4, N-KB3 2 N-KB3, P-Q4 3 P-K3, P-K3 4 B-Q3, B-K2 5 QN-Q2(a).

Cover the scoring table at the line indicated. Set up the position and make 'Black's fifth move (exposing the table just enough to read that move). Now guess White's next move, expose next line. Score par if your move agrees; if not, score zero. Make the move actually given and opponent's reply. Then guess White's next move, and so on to the end.

**COVER WHITE MOVES
IN TABLE BELOW.**   **EXPOSE ONE LINE AT A TIME**

White Played	Par Score	Black Played	Your Selection for White's move	Your Score
		5 . . . . O-O	------------------	--------
6 O-O	_____5	6 . . . . QN-Q2	------------------	--------
7 P-K4	_____7	7 . . . . PxP	------------------	--------
8 NxP	_____5	8 . . . . NxN	------------------	--------
9 BxN	_____4	9 . . . . N-B3	------------------	--------
10 B-Q3	_____5	10 . . . . P-B4	------------------	--------
11 PxP	_____6	11 . . . . BxP	------------------	--------
12 B-KN5	____6	12 . . . . B-K2	------------------	--------
13 Q-K2	_____6	13 . . . . Q-B2 (b)	------------------	--------
14 QR-Q1	___.6	14 . . . . R-Q1	------------------	---------
15 N-K5	_____7	15 . . . . B-Q2? *	------------------	--------
16 BxP† (c)	__0	16 . . . . KxB (d)	------------------	--------
17 BxN	_____9	17 . . . . BxB	------------------	--------
18 Q-R5†	_____8	18 . . . . K-N1	------------------	--------
19 QxP† (e)	__7	19 . . . . K-R2	------------------	--------
20 R-Q3	_____9	20 . . . . Resigns	------------------	--------
Total Score 100		**Your Percentage** ------------------		------

SCALE: 75-100—Excellent; 55-74—Superior; 40-54—Good; 25-39—Fair

19

Notes on COLLE vs. BUERGER

Black has been hampered from the beginning with confined Bishops. It is White's free-ranging prelates that effect the victorious combination.

Instructive to note is how Black's attempt (an unconsidered one) to get the Queen's Bishop to a more active spot is the very maneuver which leads to his defeat.

The opening has a modest appearance; nevertheless, it is superior for White because he controls more space, which is really sufficient gain to achieve from the first-move initiative.

The underlying theme of the Colle System is the retention of the White King Bishop on the diagonal poised against the Black King. As a result there is always a slight, but lasting positional bind that Black has difficulty in thwarting.

Position after 15 . . . B-Q2?

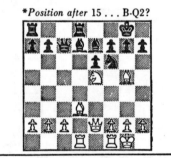

† = check; ‡ = dbl. check; § = dis. ch.

Notes to the Game

a) The system: on 4 . . . P-QB4, White sets up 5 P-QB3, to open retreat for his King Bishop and to hold his Q4, all with an eye to an early P-K4.

b) The instinctive 13 . . . P-QN3 is punished by 14 BxN, BxB 15 Q-K4, winning the Rook.

c) Nowadays, a stock combination.

d) If 16 . . . NxB 17 BxB, White wins at least the Exchange.

e) The logical goal and reward of White's combination.

SACRIFICIAL ORGY

THE IMMORTAL CAPABLANCA had a knack for making everything appear simple. He could reduce the most complex position to its bare elements and then exploit the most meager advantage to the full. Here, however, he welcomes complications with Bogolyubov (Black) as the butt of a sacrificial orgy, Moscow, 1925. The game begins with 1 P-Q4, P-Q4 2 P-QB4, P-K3 3 N-KB3, PxP 4 P-K4, P-QB4 5 BxP.

Cover scoring table at line indicated. Set up position, make Black's 5th move (exposing table just enough to read it). Guess White's move, then expose next line. Score par if your move agrees; if not, zero. Make move given, opponent's reply. Guess White's next, and so on to end.

**COVER WHITE MOVES
IN TABLE BELOW.** EXPOSE ONE LINE AT A TIME

White Played	Par Score	Black Played	Your Selection for White's move	Your Score
		5 .... PxP	----------------	--------
6 NxP _____	4	6 .... N-KB3	----------------	--------
7 N-QB3 _____	2	7 .... B-B4	----------------	--------
8 B-K3 _____	3	8 .... QN-Q2*	----------------	--------
9 BxP (a) ___	8	9 .... PxB	----------------	--------
10 NxP _____	3	10 .... Q-R4	----------------	--------
11 O-O _____	5	11 .... BxB	----------------	--------
12 PxB _____	2	12 .... K-B2	----------------	--------
13 Q-N3 _____	5	13 .... K-N3	----------------	--------
14 R-B5 _____	5	14 .... Q-N3	----------------	--------
15 N-B4† _____	5	15 .... K-R3	----------------	--------
16 P-N4 (b) __	2	16 .... P-N4	----------------	--------
17 QxQ ,_____	4	17 .... PxQ	----------------	--------
18 QR-Q1 _____	4	18 .... R-KN1 (c)	----------------	--------
19 N/4-Q5 ____	3	19 .... NxNP	----------------	--------
20 N-K7 _____	3	20 .... R-N2	----------------	--------
21 R-Q6† _____	4	21 .... K-R4	----------------	--------
22 R-B3 _____	5	22 .... N/5-B3	----------------	--------
23 R-R3† _____	3	23 .... K-N5	----------------	--------
24 R-N3† _____	3	24 .... K-R4	----------------	--------
25 N-B5 _____	4	25 .... R-N3	----------------	--------
26 N-K7 (d) __	3	26 .... P-N5	----------------	--------
27 NxR _____	3	27 .... KxN	----------------	--------
28 RxP† _____	4	28 .... K-B2	----------------	--------
29 R-B4 _____	4	29 .... K-N2	----------------	--------
30 P-K5 _____	4	30 .... N-K1	----------------	--------
31 R-K6 _____	5	31 .... Resigns (e)	----------------	--------
Total Score	**100**	Your Percentage	--------------------	

SCALE: 75-100—Excellent; 55-74—Superior; 40-54—Good; 25-39—Fair

Notes on CAPABLANCA vs. BOGOLYUBOV

Capablanca, confident of his unequaled positional strategy in all parts of the game, once declared: "I can draw at will against any master." Meaning, of course, there was no player alive able ever to defeat him.

Bogolyubov was even less modest. He said: "When I have the White pieces, I win because I am playing White. When I have the Black pieces I win because I am Bogolyubov."

Despite the exchange of Queens in this game, Black remains in constant danger. In order to defend his monarch, Bogolyubov must shuttle his pieces about in the two back rows, impeding the development of his Queen Rook and Bishop. Finally, a Knight is picked off and with it the game.

Position after 8 ... QN-Q2

NOTES TO THE GAME

a) An extraordinary positional sacrifice of a piece in the opening.

b) Give yourself bonus of 8 points if you had forced win which White missed: 16 Q-B7, P-N3 17 P-KN4, QxP† 18 K-N2, PxR 19 P-N5†, KxP 20 Q-N7†, KxN 21 R-B1†, K-K4 22 Q-K7†, K-Q5 23 R-Q1†, K-B5 24 Q-K6†, K-B4 25 P-N4†, KxP 26 Q-N3†, K any 27 Q-N5 mate.

c) Simplification by 18 . . . PxN leaves White in uphill battle after 19 P-N5†, K-N2 20 PxN†, NxP 21 R-N5†, K-B2 22 PxP.

d) 26 R-R3† is more forceful. White expected repetition here to gain time on the clock.

e) Or 31 . . . N-B2 32 R-K7† and 33 P-K6.

SPIELMANN OUTSPIELMANNED

WHEN the master of sacrifice meets the mighty Capablanca, what happens? He merely meets his master as evinced in the following Queen Pawn Game from the New York International Tournament of 1927. Capa (White) shows Spielmann how it is done! He gives till it hurts—Spielmann. The game begins with 1 P-Q4, P-Q4 2 N-KB3, P-K3 3 P-B4, N-Q2 4 N-B3, KN-B3 5 B-N5.

Cover scoring table at line indicated. Set up position, make Black's 5th move (exposing table just enough to read it). Guess White's move, then expose next line. Score par if your move agrees; if not, zero. Make move given, opponent's reply. Guess White's next, and so on to end.

COVER WHITE MOVES IN TABLE BELOW.   **EXPOSE ONE LINE AT A TIME**

White Played	Par Score	Black Played	Your Selection for White's move	Your Score
		5 . . . . B–N5 (a)	-----------------	--------
6 PxP	4	6 . . . . PxP	-----------------	--------
7 Q-R4	5	7 . . . . BxN†	-----------------	--------
8 PxB	3	8 . . . . O–O	-----------------	--------
9 P–K3	3	9 . . . . P–B4	-----------------	--------
10 B–Q3	4	10 . . . . P–B5	-----------------	--------
11 B–B2	4	11 . . . . Q–K2	-----------------	--------
12 O–O	4	12 . . . . P–QR3	-----------------	--------
13 KR–K1 (b)	6	13 . . . . Q–K3	-----------------	--------
14 N–Q2	5	14 . . . . P–QN4	-----------------	--------
15 Q–R5 (c)	7	15 . . . . N–K5	-----------------	--------
16 NxN	4	16 . . . . PxN	-----------------	--------
17 P–QR4	6	17 . . . . Q–Q4*	-----------------	--------
18 PxP (d)	9	18 . . . . QxB	-----------------	--------
19 BxP	6	19 . . . . R–N1 (e)	-----------------	--------
20 PxP	5	20 . . . . R–N4	-----------------	--------
21 Q–B7	6	21 . . . . N–N3	-----------------	--------
22 P–R7	4	22 . . . . B–R6	-----------------	--------
23 KR–N1	6	23 . . . . RxR†	-----------------	--------
24 RxR	3	24 . . . . P–B4	-----------------	--------
25 B–B3	3	25 . . . . P–B5	-----------------	--------
26 PxP	3	26 . . . . Resigns	-----------------	--------
Total Score 100		Your Percentage -----------------		

SCALE: 75-100—Excellent; 55-74—Superior; 40-54—Good; 25-39—Fair

23

Notes on CAPABLANCA vs. SPIELMANN

We can imagine that this victory gave Capablanca more lasting pleasure than any of those other wins against grandmasters which were produced through delicate positional play.

The combination here is unique in the literature of chess games. Where else can one find a Rook's Pawn on the sixth rank stronger than a Queen? There is the charm of a fairy tale here. Jack-the-Giant-Killer (the Queen's Rook's Pawn) sneaking past the enemy's flank to victory and fame! (With a bit of help from the famous Cuban.)

Considering the game less romantically, Spielmann's defeat stems from the non-development of his Queen-side.

Motto for this game: "And the meek shall inherit the earth."

Position after 17 . . . Q–Q4

NOTES TO THE GAME

a) The Manhattan Variation which enjoyed its vogue, then disappeared into innocuous desuetude.

b) White intends P–K4, to disrupt the Black forces. But Black concocts a counter.

c) White destroys the counter as will become evident later on.

d) The point, and an unpleasant surprise for Black. Black is lost.

e) On 19 . . . R–R2, White wins with 20 P–N6, QxQ 21 PxR.

A PAWN'S WORTH

World Champion Smyslov is known to be generally a very solid, conservative player. Here, however, as White against J. H. Donner, Venice, 1950, he squanders Pawns in a fashion which justifies the popular newspaper phraseology, "a mere Pawn on the chessboard." And "justifies" is right, for Smyslov reaps a handsome harvest. Donner's defense becomes impotent. This French Defense starts with the moves: 1 P–K4, P–K3 2 P–Q4, P–Q4 3 N–QB3, N–KB3 4 B–N5, B–N5 (a) 5 P–K5, P–KR3 6 B–Q2.

Cover scoring table at line indicated. Set up position, make Black's next move (exposing table just enough to read it). Now guess White's 7th move, then expose it. Score par if move agrees; zero if not. Make move actually given, opponent's reply. Then guess White's next, and so on.

COVER WHITE MOVES

IN TABLE BELOW.   EXPOSE ONE LINE AT A TIME

White Played	Par Score	Black Played	Your Selection for White's move	Your Score
		6 .... BxN	---------------	--------
7 PxB	_____4	7 .... N–K5	---------------	--------
8 Q–N4	_____5	8 .... P–KN3 (b)	---------------	--------
9 B–B1 (c)	__6	9 .... NxQBP	---------------	--------
10 B–Q3	_____4	10 .... P–QB4	---------------	------.-
11 PxP	_____4	11 .... N–B3 (d)	---------------	--------
12 N–B3	_____4	12 .... Q–R4 (e)	---------------	--------
13 O–O	_____4	13 .... QxBP (f)	---------------	--------
14 Q–KR4	___5	14 .... N–K2 (g)	---------------	--------
15 Q–B6	_____4	15 .... R–R2	---------------	--------
16 P–QR4	___6	16 .... Q–B2	---------------	--------
17 B–R3	_____4	17 .... N–K5	---------------	--------
18 KBxN	_____3	18 .... PxB	---------------	--------
19 N–Q2	_____3	19 .... N–Q4	---------------	--------
20 Q–R4	_____2	20 .... QxKP	---------------	--------
21 NxP	_____6	21 .... P–KN4	---------------	--------
22 Q–N4	_____2	22 .... B–Q2	---------------	--------
23 N–Q6†	_____4	23 .... K–Q1	---------------	--------
24 NxNP†	___4	24 .... K–B1	---------------	--------
25 N–Q6†	_____4	25 .... K–B2	---------------	--------
26 Q–B4†	_____4	26 .... B–B3	---------------	--------
27 Q–B5	_____7	27 .... Q–B5	---------------	--------
28 P–B4	_____5	28 .... N–N3	---------------	--------
29 P–R5*	_____6	.... Resigns (h)	---------------	--------

Total Score 100 | Your Percentage _____ _____

SCALE: 75-100—Excellent; 55-74—Superior; 40-54—Good; 25-39—Fair

25

Notes on SMYSLOV vs. DONNER

The keynote of White's strategy is to plant a Bishop at QR3. Therefore, he gives up a Pawn on move 9 B–B1 in order not to exchange this piece.

Throughout the opening skirmishes, Black's tactics are extremely dubious. He is burdened with:

1. Weak black squares over which the enemy Bishop can penetrate.
2. A Rook without a future at KR2.
3. A perilous King position which is the consequence of 1 and 2.

Against a master of Smyslov's caliber such indifferent shuttling is sharply punished.

This is one of Smyslov's pet lines and soon Donner (the Hollander) finds himself "in Dutch."

Position after 29 P-R5

NOTES TO THE GAME

a) The McCutcheon Variation: *MCO*: p. 99.
b) 8 . . . K-B1 gives inferior chances.
c) The first Pawn but a "book" one. Equal credit also for 9 B-Q3; 4 for 9 N-B3 or 9 B-K3.
d) One way to equality is 11 . . . Q-B2 12 N-B3, N-Q2 13 B-K3, NxBP. Score 4 for 11 B-Q2.
e) Not now 12 . . . Q-B2 13 O-O, NxP? 14 Q-Q4!
f) In the see-saw of Pawn captures, White is again one down; but 13 . . . Q-R5 with aim to swap Queens has been recommended.
g) Now Black is in trouble: on 14 . . . Q-K2, 15 B-N5 and 16 B-B6 is too strong.
h) Black loses at least a piece after 29 . . . N-B1 or N-Q2 and 30 N-N5†.

†=check; ‡=double check; §=discovered check

26

INVOKING THE PAST

When a grandmaster is intent on winning at all costs, he will often resort to one of the outmoded classical debuts which grant room for combination, maneuver and blunder. At Zaandam, 1946, Hungarian Szabo (White) initiates this Scotch Gambit and Dutch master Muhring is the victim. The game begins with 1 P–K4, P–K4 2 N–KB3, N–QB3 3 P–Q4, PxP 4 B–B4, N–B3 5 O–O (*MCO*: page 54, col. 11; but see note *a*).

Cover scoring table at line indicated. Set up position, make Black's next move (exposing table just enough to read it). Now guess White's 6th move, then expose it. Score par, if move agrees; zero, if not. Make move actually given, opponent's reply. Then guess White's next, and so on.

COVER WHITE MOVES

IN TABLE BELOW. EXPOSE ONE LINE AT A TIME

White Played	Par Score	Black Played	Your Selection for White's move	Your Score
		5 . . . . NxP		
6 R–K1	3	6 . . . . P–Q4		
7 BxP	3	7 . . . . QxB		
8 N–B3	3	8 . . . . Q–KR4? (b)		
9 NxN	3	9 . . . . B–K3		
10 B–N5 (c)	5	10 . . . . P–KR3		
11 B–B6!	7	11 . . . . Q–Q4		
12 P–B3	4	12 . . . . P–Q6		
13 N–Q4	4	13 . . . . NxN		
14 PxN	4	14 . . . . Q–QR4		
15 QxP	4	15 . . . . B–QN5		
16 P–Q5!	6	16 . . . . QxQP (d)		
17 Q–KN3	5	17 . . . . BxR		
18 RxB	4	18 . . . . Q–QR4		
19 B–B3	4	19 . . . . Q–Q4		
20 QxBP	6	20 . . . . R–Q1		
21 B–N4	5	21 . . . . R–Q2		
22 Q–N3	5	22 . . . . P–B3		
23 Q–N8† (e)*	3	23 . . . . K–B2 (f)		
24 QxR	5	24 . . . . R–Q1		
25 Q–R7	4	25 . . . . B–B4		
26 N–N5†	8	26 . . . . BPxN		
27 R–K7†	5	27 . . . . Resigns		

Total Score 100 | Your Percentage _____

SCALE: 75-100—Excellent; 55-74—Superior; 40-54—Good; 25-39—Fair

Notes on SZABO vs. MUHRING

Seven moves with the Black Queen out of the first nineteen! Surely, something is amiss in the Black defense. Black's 5 . . . NxP (given as equalizing by some annotators) is questionable, mainly because of psychological reasons. The open file created promotes the type of game Szabo had been hoping for.

White gains too much momentum from Black's risky sally, and Black would be better advised to have played more modestly: 5 . . . P–Q3 followed by . . . B–K2 and . . . 0–0. Cramped, but sound. White has some initiative but not enough to decide the issue as he does here as early as 16 P–Q5!

Open-board play is favorable to Szabo's style. White's command of the King file and his menacing Bishop, preventing castling, confirm the victory.

Position after 23 Q-N8†

NOTES TO THE GAME

a) This position can also arise from any one of the following openings: Bishop's Opening, Petroff Defense and Two Knights Defense; and the Giuoco Piano and Max Lange can come in by transpositions: i.e., 5 . . . B-B4. A most curious nexus of openings!

b) 8 . . . Q-QR4 is supposedly better.

c) To prevent Queen-side castling.

d) Relatively best: 16 . . . BxR 17 PxB gives White an irresistible attack.

e) 23 N-B5 is correct (take 6 points for it).

f) 23 . . . R-Q1 barely holds.

---

†=check; ‡=double check; §=discovered check

28

A CURIOUS MONSTER

How far ahead does the master see over the chessboard? Probably, two or three moves. The rest is experience, judgment, intuition or the divine afflatus, call it what you will. Here, in an offhand encounter played many years ago, the great Alekhine (White) rips into the French Defense of Grigorieff and produces a freak, a game with five Queens. Did he foresee the result? Likely not. But he predicted it. The opening moves are: 1 P–K4, P–K3 2 P–Q4, P–Q4 3 N–QB3, N–KB3 4 B–N5.

Cover scoring table at line indicated. Set up position, make Black's next move (exposing table just enough to read it). Now guess White's 5th move, then expose it. Score par, if move agrees; zero, if not. Make move actually given, opponent's reply. Then guess White's next, and so on.

COVER WHITE MOVES

IN TABLE BELOW.   EXPOSE ONE LINE AT A TIME

White Played	Par Score	Black Played	Your Selection for White's move	Your Score
		4 .... B–N5	----------------	--------
5 P–K5	3	5 .... P–KR3	----------------	--------
6 PxN (a)	2	6 .... PxB	----------------	--------
7 PxP	3	7 .... R–N1	----------------	--------
8 P–KR4	4	8 .... PxP	----------------	--------
9 Q–N4	4	9 .... B–K2	----------------	--------
10 P–KN3	5	10 .... P–QB4	----------------	--------
11 PxRP	4	11 .... PxP*	----------------	--------
12 P–R5 (b)	6	12 .... PxN	----------------	--------
13 P–R6	5	13 .... PxP	----------------	--------
14 R–N1	4	14 .... Q–R4†	----------------	--------
15 K–K2	5	15 .... QxP	----------------	--------
16 P–R7	6	16 .... QxR	----------------	--------
17 PxR(Q)†	4	17 .... K–Q2	----------------	--------
18 Q/N8xP	4	18 .... QxP†	----------------	--------
19 K–B3	4	19 .... N–B3	----------------	--------
20 Q/N4xP†	4	20 .... K–B2	----------------	--------
21 Q–B4†	4	21 .... K–N3	----------------	--------
22 Q/K6–K3†	4	22 .... B–B4	----------------	--------
23 P–N8(Q)	5	23 .... P–N8(Q)(c)	----------------	--------
24 R–R6 (d)	7	24 .... QxB	----------------	--------
25 Q–N4†	5	25 .... Q–N4	----------------	--------
26 Q–Q8†	4	26 .... K–R3	----------------	--------
27 Q/K3–R3†	4	27 .... Resigns (e)	----------------	--------

Total Score   100 | Your Percentage ---------------------

SCALE: 75-100—Excellent; 55-74—Superior; 40-54—Good; 25-39—Fair

Notes on ALEKHINE vs. GRIGORIEFF

A surrealist chess nightmare featuring a quintet of Queens. This queenly bravura attains such fantasy that its very authenticity is questioned by Buschke.

Alekhine, the creator of hundreds of intriguing games in which Queens die regularly, may be forgiven for here creating one that gives birth to many.

Did this happen or did Alekhine cook it up? Alas, "the greatest chess-player of all time" is not alive to say. Because of this game, however, Grigorieff's name will not be forgotten in the annals of chess.

A curious point about the opening, a French Defense: The result is either a deadly draw (the Exchange Variation) or a slam-bang melee, during which anything can happen.

*Position after 11 ... PxP

NOTES TO THE GAME

Provide yourself with substitute Queens in order to follow this game: two extra White Queens, one extra Black Queen.

a) Usual is 6 B-K2, for which take 4 point credit. The text move is wild and speculative.

b) A profound gamble.

c) Here are five Queens on the board at one time, strange as it may seem.

d) White threatens mate in one! See it?

e) The authenticity of this game has been challenged by A. Buschke.

---

†=check; ‡=double check; §=discovered check

30

WHAT HAPPENED TO MICKEY MOUSE?

A couple of decades, it seems, is sufficient to go from limelight to obscurity. Master Mikenas (formerly nicknamed Mickey Mouse) certainly traversed that path. When he was on top, his brilliance was blinding. Here at Gruzinske, 1941, in the staid Queen's Gambit, he downs Lebedew with a dazzling sacrificial orgy. The game begins with 1 P–Q4, N–KB3 2 P–QB4, P–K3 3 N–QB3, P–Q4 4 B–N5.

Cover scoring table at line indicated. Set up position, make Black's next move (exposing table just enough to read it). Now guess White's 4th move, then expose it. Score par, if move agrees; zero, if not. Make move actually given, Black's reply. Then guess White's next, and so on.

COVER WHITE MOVES IN TABLE BELOW.   **EXPOSE ONE LINE AT A TIME**

White Played	Par Score	Black Played	Your Selection for White's move	Your Score
		4 .... B–K2	....	....
5 P–K3	 2	5 .... P–KR3	....	....
6 B–R4	 2	6 .... O–O	....	....
7 R–B1	 2	7 .... P–B3	....	....
8 B–Q3	 2	8 .... QN–Q2	....	....
9 N–B3	 2	9 .... PxP	....	....
10 BxP	 2	10 .... N–Q4 (a)	....	....
11 B–KN3! (b)	4	11 .... NxN	....	....
12 PxN	 3	12 .... P–QB4	....	....
13 O–O	 2	13 .... P–QR3	....	....
14 B–Q3	 5	14 .... N–B3	....	....
15 N–K5	 3	15 .... B–Q3?	....	....
16 B–R4	 5	16 .... B–K2	....	....
17 B–N1 (c)	.. 6	17 .... Q–K1	....	....
18 PxP	 5	18 .... P–KN4	....	....
19 B–N3	 2	19 .... BxP	....	....
20 P–KB4! ·(d)	7	20 .... BxP†	....	....
21 K–R1	 3	21 .... BxR	....	....
22 PxP!! (e)	. 8	22 .... BxP	....	....
23 RxN	 6	23 .... K–N2	....	....
24 Q–Q3	 5	24 .... P–KR4	....	....
25 P–KR4	 5	25 .... KxR *	....	..... ·· ··
26 N–N4†	 6	26 .... PxN	....	....
27 B–K5†	 7	27 .... KxB	....	....
28 Q–Q4 mate	6			

Total Score   100 | Your Percentage -------------------

SCALE: 75-100—Excellent; 55-74—Superior; 40-54—Good; 25-39—Fair

Notes on MIKENAS vs. LEBEDEW

Mikenas' bravura is the ideal. Every chess-player's dream game. Even the most sophisticated practitioners of positional strong-point play, to whom flashy sacrifices are banal, must admire the fireworks.

The artistic crux of the combination is the seeming loss of *tempo* by the attacker when Black's Bishop checks the King on move 20. No matter, Black's house is already undermined.

Wherever brilliancies are discussed, Mikenas' masterpiece must be included.

What can one say of Lebedew? An obscure player from somewhere in Central Europe? A coffeehouse professional? A talented amateur? Who knows?

One thing we are certain of. Lebedew has been immortalized by Mikenas. Another way of attaining fame through the back door.

Chess has had many such examples.

*Position after 25 . . . KxR

NOTES TO THE GAME

a) 10 . . . P-QN4 11 B-Q3, P-QR3, followed by . . . P-B4 is the best way of liberating Black's problem Bishop.

b) This move, made possible and good only because of 5 . . . P-KR3, exercises a fine bind on the position.

c) Inaugurating the standard King-side assault. A later Q-Q3 threatens BxN and Q-R7 mate.

d) A great conception.

e) The real point. But there is more, much more.

---

† = check; ‡ = double check; § = dis. check

DOUBLE THREAT, DOUBLE TROUBLE

When Tartakover (White) meets Najdorf, it is as sure as mate that there will be pyrotechnics. Certainly, here, in a set match in Poland, 1935, these mighty gladiators are as good as their reputation. The finale is a double threat, sockdolager. The opening, a Queen Pawn Game, begins with 1 P–Q4, N–KB3 2 N–KB3, P–QN3 3 P–K3.

Cover scoring table at line indicated. Set up position, make Black's next move (exposing table just enough to read it). Now guess White's 4th move, then expose it. Score par, if move agrees; zero, if not. Make move actually given, Black's reply. Then guess White's next, and so on.

COVER WHITE MOVES
IN TABLE BELOW.   EXPOSE ONE LINE AT A TIME

White Played	Par Score	Black Played	Your Selection for White's move	Your Score
		3 .... B–N2	....	....
4 B–Q3	4	4 .... P–B4	....	....
5 QN–Q2	4	5 .... P–K3	....	....
6 O–O	4	6 .... B–K2	....	....
7 R–K1	5	7 .... PxP	....	....
8 PxP	4	8 .... O–O	....	....
9 P–QN3	5	9 .... N–B3	....	....
10 P–B4	5	10 .... P–Q4	....	....
11 B–N2	5	11 .... R–B1 (a)	....	....
12 QR–B1	5	12 .... B–N5	....	....
13 P–QR3	5	13 .... PxP	....	....
14 PxP	4	14 .... BxN	....	....
15 QxB	4	15 .... N–QR4	....	....
16 Q–K3	5	16 .... N–Q2	....	....
17 N–K5	6	17 .... R–K1 (b)	....	....
18 P–Q5 (c)	..8	18 .... N–B1 (d)	....	....
19 Q–N3	8	19 .... P–B3	....	....
20 N–N4	9	20 .... K–R1 * (e)	....	....
21 QBxP	10	21 .... Resigns (f)	....	....
Total Score	100	Your Percentage _____		

SCALE: 75-100—Excellent; 55-74—Superior; 40-54—Good; 25-39—Fair

Notes on TARTAKOVER vs. NAJDORF

Tartakover was always a sharp competitor. Unorthodoxy to the point of eccentricity in the opening and a determined jauntiness in mid-game tactics carried him to many a victory.

During the New York Tourney, 1924, during one of the free days Tartakover visited the Zoo. The next afternoon he sat down with Marshall and played 1 P–QN4. He dubbed this the "Ourang-Outan." The great Alekhine was not at all impressed with the idea: "Provides Black with no difficulties in development and only makes more difficult White's future fight for the center."

Once Najdorf came to New York, unknown and unannounced. He strolled into one of the minor clubs where the odds-giving sharpshooters offered Knight or Rook for a dollar a game.

Najdorf, looking like a meek pushover, accepted a Rook from the pride and bulwark of 42nd Street. A score of kibitzers could never understand how this humble stranger always just managed to win by the most minimal means, an extra move that assured the queening of a Pawn.

*Position after 20 ... K–R1

NOTES TO THE GAME

a) Tartakover suggests 11 . . . N-KR4.

b) 17 . . . NxN is the move. If 18 PxN, the long diagonal is closed. If 18 QxN, Q-B2.

c) Now the long diagonal is opened.
d) If 18 . . . PxP, 19 B-B5.

e) 20 . . . N-N3 is met by 21 BxN, PxB 22 NxP†, PxN 23 QxP†, etc.

f) Mate and Queen! after 21 . . . PxB 22 N-R6!

---

† = check; ‡ = double check; § = dis. check

34

A STAR IS CONFIRMED

Stockholm 1962 confirms pre-eminence of a new star. Bobby Fischer, Brooklyn's boy wonder, has come of age. His technique in all departments of the game is a model of perfection. Here as White in a Sicilian against Olafsson, he latches on to a minimal in opening initiative, converts this to a pesky, passed Pawn in mid-game and is about to promote it in the end-game when Black resigns. The game begins: 1 P–K4, P–QB4 2 N–KB3, P–Q3 3 P–Q4, PxP 4 NxP, N–KB3 5 N–QB3, N–B3 6 B–QB4.

Cover scoring table at line indicated. Set up position, make Black's next move (exposing table just enough to read it). Now *guess* White's 7th move, then expose it. Score par, if move agrees; zero, if not. Make move actually given, Black's reply. Then guess White's next, and so on.

**COVER WHITE MOVES
IN TABLE BELOW.**   **EXPOSE ONE LINE AT A TIME**

White Played	Par Score	Black Played	Your Selection for White's move	Your Score
		6 .... P–K3	....	....
7 B–N3	 4	7 .... B–K2	....	....
8 P–B4	 4	8 .... O–O	....	....
9 B–K3	 3	9 .... NxN (a)	....	....
10 BxN	 2	10 .... P–QN4	....	....
11 P–K5 (b)	. 4	11 .... PxP	....	....
12 PxP	 2	12 .... N–Q2	....	....
13 O–O	 3	13 .... P–N5	....	....
14 N–K4	 4	14 .... B–N2	....	....
15 N–Q6 (c)	. 5	15 .... BxN	....	....
16 PxB	 2	16 .... Q–N4	....	....
17 Q–K2	 3	17 .... B–Q4 (d)	....	....
18 QR–Q1	... 3	18 .... BxB	....	....
19 RPxB	 3	19 .... P–K4	....	....
20 Q–N5	 5	20 .... P–QR3 (e)	....	....
21 QxN	 3	21 .... PxB	....	....
22 Q–B5	 5	22 .... QxQ (f)	....	....
23 RxQ	 2	23 .... KR–Q1	....	....
24 RxQP	 2	24 .... QR–B1	....	....
25 R–B2	 3	25 .... P–QR4	....	....
26 R/2–Q2	... 3	26 .... P–B3	....	....
27 R–QB4	... 4	27 .... K–B2	....	....
28 R–B7†	 5	28 .... K–N3	....	....
29 R–K7	5	29 .... P–R4	....	....
30 P–Q7	5	30 .... R–B2 *	....	....
31 P–B4	 7	31 .... K–R2	....	....
32 P–R4	 4	32 .... K–N3	....	....
33 R–Q5	5	33 .... Resigns	....	....
Total Score 100		**Your Percentage**		————

SCALE: 75-100—Excellent; 55-74—Superior; 40-54—Good; 25-39—Fair

Notes on FISCHER vs. OLAFSSON

Concurrent with Bobby Fischer's surge from stripling to aspirant for the world title is the chess career of Fridrick Olafsson. Had not Fischer's exploits captured the major interest of the chess world, the blond Icelander's talents would, no doubt, have been more widely appreciated.

Olafsson's reputation has been overshadowed by the American's fame. Olafsson, however, is happy that it was he alone who put the chess spotlight on little, mist-shrouded Iceland, whose entire population could be tucked away into a corner of the borough of Manhattan without making too much disturbance in the traffic problem.

In this game Fischer has not yet rejected the idea of his King Bishop occupying the classical diagonal, pointing at the adverse weak spot, Black's KB2. In two games of the unfinished match with Reshevsky, Fischer employed the Bishop maneuver. Finding it unsatisfactory later, he played this Bishop to K2.

Fischer's end-game technique is the simplicity of ruthless logic.

*Position after 30 . . . R–B2

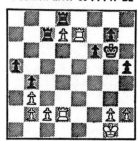

Notes to the Game

a) Double-edged—the exchange centralizes the White Bishop but permits a counter on the wing.

b) The center Pawns act first.

c) This is a move of refined judgment, compelling the following exchange and leaving White with a powerful, passed, center Pawn.

d) Black panics. He ought to retain his Bishop for counterplay. Not 17 . . . KR–Q1 18 RxP! though.

e) This move costs a Pawn, but Black has no adequate move.

f) He certainly ought to retain his Queen.

---

† = check; ‡ = double check; § = dis. check

THE SUCCULENT YEARS

In his heyday, the Great Denker could make a dope out of any grand-master. Courage, confidence and abandon were his forte. Here, as White at the United States Championship of 1944 in New York city, he abandons a Pawn against the mighty Fine and introduces complications which finally net him the game. The opening, a Nimzo-Indian, begins with 1 P–Q4, N–KB3 2 P–QB4, P–K3 3 N–QB3, B–N5 4 P–K3, P–QN3 5 B–Q3.

Cover scoring table at line indicated. Set up position, make Black's next move (exposing table just enough to read it). Now guess White's 6th move, then expose it. Score par, if move agrees; zero, if not. Make move actually given, Black's reply. Then guess White's next, and so on.

COVER WHITE MOVES
IN TABLE BELOW.   EXPOSE ONE LINE AT A TIME

White Played	Par Score	Black Played	Your Selection for White's move	Your Score
		5 .... B–N2	....	....
6 N–B3 3		6 .... N–K5	....	....
7 O–O (a) ...6		7 .... NxN	....	....
8 PxN 3		8 .... BxP	....	....
9 R–N1 3		9 .... B–R4	....	....
10 B–R3 6		10 .... P–Q3	....	....
11 P–B5 7		11 .... O–O	....	....
12 PxQP 4		12 .... PxP	....	....
13 P–K4 5		13 .... R–K1	....	....
14 P–K5 5		14 .... PxP	....	....
15 NxP 6		15 .... Q–N4 (b)	....	....
16 P–N3 3		16 .... P–N3	....	....
17 Q–R4 7		17 .... Q–Q1	....	....
18 KR–B1 5		18 .... P–QN4 (c)	....	....
19 BxQNP 5		19 .... Q–Q4	....	....
20 P–B3 3		20 .... B–N3 * (d)	....	....
21 R–B5!! 8		21 .... BxR (e)	....	....
22 BxB 5		22 .... R–KB1	....	....
23 B–B4 6		23 .... B–B3	....	....
24 BxQ 5		24 .... BxQ	....	....
25 BxQR 5		25 .... Resigns	....	....
Total Score 100		Your Percentage		

SCALE: 75-100—Excellent; 55-74—Superior; 40-54—Good; 25-39—Fair

Notes on DENKER vs. FINE

This was the most important game of the U. S. Championship Tournament of 1944, an unexpected setback for grandmaster Fine who had been favored to cop first prize. Denker, playing brilliantly throughout the championship test, finished in front, a full point ahead of Fine.

Black's early grab of a Pawn seems ill-advised. For many moves his King Bishop occupies an awkward post where it hardly matters for offense or defense. No doubt, Fine speculated on his superior experience and technique to get off scot-free with this violation of tactics.

Eventually, Black even works up a semi-frightening counter-attack with Queen and Queen Bishop, but Denker has a saving move, 20 P–B3. At this point Black is behind in development, his Queen Knight still munching in the stable. White's 21 R–B5 is a sad disillusionment for Black, who, with two Bishops and Queen poised along the big diagonals against the White King, might seem to be making a fight of it. But White's Rook brutally places the situation in its true light.

*Position after 20 . . . B–N3

NOTES TO THE GAME

a) Here White offers a gambit. It is probably best declined over-the-board.

b) The decisive mistake. According to Fine, 15 . . . P–N3 holds.

c) Or 18 . . . N–R3 19 QxB!! PxQ 20 RxB, N–N5 21 BxN, PxB 22 NxBP, Q–B3 23 R/B–B7, Q–N2 24 N–K5, Q–R3 25 N–N4, and White wins.

d) Hoping for 21 BxR, QxN 22 RxB? Q–K6†.

e) 21 . . . QxRP is relatively best.

† = check; ‡ = double check; § = dis. check

WHEN THE INVINCIBLE MEETS THE IMMORTAL

When master of position play meets master of attack, what happens? One answer is recorded here in Nimzovich vs. Spielmann, Hamburg 1910. All poised for onslaught, Spielmann (Black) finds his prospects vanish into thin air, somehow, and the issue is reduced to one of good and bad Pawns, plus a tail-end tactical switch. The opening, a Scotch, begins with 1 P–K4, P–K4 2 N–KB3, N–QB3 3 P–Q4, PxP 4 NxP, N–B3 5 N–QB3, B–N5 6 NxN.

Cover scoring table at line indicated. Set up position, make Black's next move (exposing table just enough to read it). Now guess White's 7th move, then expose it. Score par, if move agrees; zero, if not. Make move actually given, Black's reply. Then guess White's next, and so on.

COVER WHITE MOVES
IN TABLE BELOW.   EXPOSE ONE LINE AT A TIME

White Played	Par Score	Black Played		Your Selection for White's move	Your Score
		6	NPxN	. . . .	. . . .
7 B–Q3	3	7	P–Q4	. . . .	. . . .
8 PxP	3	8	PxP	. . . .	. . . .
9 O–O	3	9	O–O	. . . .	. . . .
10 B–KN5	3	10	P–B3	. . . .	. . . .
11 N–K2 (a)	. .5	11	R–K1	. . . .	. . . .
12 N–Q4	4	12	Q–Q3	. . . .	. . . .
13 Q–B3	4	13	N–K5	. . . .	. . . .
14 B–K3	3	14	B–Q2	. . . .	. . . .
15 QR–Q1	4	15	Q–N3	. . . .	. . . .
16 P–KR3	3	16	B–Q3	. . . .	. . . .
17 B–B1	3	17	R–K2 (b)	. . . .	. . . .
18 P–B4	4	18	P–QB4	. . . .	. . . .
19 N–K2	3	19	P–Q5	. . . .	. . . .
20 B–B4	4	20	B–B3	. . . .	. . . .
21 N–N3	5	21	BxB	. . . .	. . . .
22 QxB	3	22	NxN	. . . .	. . . .
23 PxN (c)	. .5	23	Q–K3?	. . . .	. . . .
24 Q–B5 (d)	. .6	24	P–N3	. . . .	. . . .
25 QxBP	4	25	R–Q1	. . . .	. . . .
26 K–R2	3	26	Q–Q2	. . . .	. . . .
27 R–B4	5	27	R–K3*	. . . .	. . . .
28 BxP!	8	28	R–K7 (e)	. . . .	. . . .
29 BxP†	4	29	K–N2	. . . .	. . . .
30 Q–N5†	4	30	K–B1	. . . .	. . . .
31 B–R5§	4	31	Resigns	. . . .	. . . .

Total Score 100 | Your Percentage . . . .

SCALE: 75-100—Excellent; 55-74—Superior; 40-54—Good; 25-39—Fair

Notes on NIMZOVICH vs. SPIELMANN

Nimzovich, the author of *My System*, a book which has irritated many open-board tacticians, gives Spielmann a bit of Spielmann's own medicine.

It is not Spielmann, the champion of the combination at any cost, who makes the initial sacrifice, but "hypermodern" Nimzo, usually concerned with strong-point and weak-point Pawn skeletons.

The game is another example of Lasker's ruling: "Correct strategy presents the sounder player with the most potent tactical opportunities. 'Combinations' are never to be forced. They always arise from the opponent's errors."

Spielmann's weakness was to create fireworks willy-nilly, while his own house was burning down. Nevertheless his chess career produced more wins than losses despite a tendency for over-extended positions.

Nimzovich was a better dissembler. Cunning, indirect, a master of camouflage, had his technique equaled his intellect, he might have been world champion.

* Position after 27 ... R–K3

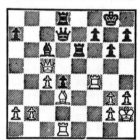

NOTES TO THE GAME

a) 11 Q–B3 is an alternative move more in vogue now.

b) Black's development is superior. His Pawn position, however, requires careful nursing.

c) Of course not 23 BxQ on account of 23 ... N–K7†.

d) This simultaneous attack on two Pawns wins one by force by the curious happenstance that the defense 24 ... QxQ is actually no defense.

e) The point is that, on 28 ... (either) PxB, 29 R/4xP wins.

---

† = check; ‡ = double check; § = dis. check

THE CATALAN IS OUT OF THE BAG

At the great tournament of Saltsjoebaden 1948, the Catalan Opening was in vogue. Here the Hungarian L. Szabo employs it against the Finnish Eero Book in what is purported to be Book's "patented defense." Book had not lost a single game with it. There is always a first time! The game begins: 1 N–KB3, P–Q4 2 P–KN3, N–KB3 3 B–N2, P–K3 4 O–O.

Cover scoring table at line indicated. Set up position, make Black's next move (exposing table just enough to read it). Now guess White's 5th move, then expose it. Score par, if move agrees; zero, if not. Make move actually given, Black's reply. Then guess White's next, and so on.

COVER WHITE MOVES IN TABLE BELOW.

EXPOSE ONE LINE AT A TIME

White Played	Par Score	Black Played	Your Selection for White's move	Your Score
		4 .... B–K2	....	....
5 P–B4 4		5 .... O–O	....	....
6 P–Q4 4		6 .... P–B3	....	....
7 N–B3 4		7 .... P–QN3	....	....
8 N–K5 5		8 .... B–R3	....	....
9 PxP 4		9 .... BPxP	....	....
10 B–B4 4		10 .... KN–Q2	....	....
11 R–B1 (a) ..4		11 .... NxN	....	....
12 BxN 4		12 .... P–QN4 (b)	....	....
13 P–K4 7		13 .... P–N5	....	....
14 N–K2 4		14 .... Q–R4	....	....
15 PxP 4		15 .... PxP	....	....
16 N–B4 6		16 .... BxR *	....	....
17 Q–N4 7		17 .... P–N3 (c)	....	....
18 BxP 8		18 .... B–Q6	....	....
19 BxR 5		19 .... B–KB4	....	....
20 Q–K2 4		20 .... B–N4	....	....
21 P–KR4 5		21 .... BxN	....	....
22 BxB 4		22 .... N–Q2	....	....
23 B–B3 5		23 .... B–K3	....	....
24 B–Q6! 8		24 .... Resigns (d)	....	....
Total Score 100		Your Percentage		

SCALE: 75-100—Excellent; 55-74—Superior; 40-54—Good; 25-39—Fair

Notes on SZABO vs. BOOK

Is not this contest between a Hungarian and a Finn, played in Sweden, in which the players adopted an opening named after a Spanish province, proof of the royal game's cosmopolitan appeal?

English type cannot find equivalents for the sound of the Finnish master's name, which should be pronounced somewhat like "Burk" (rhymes with "Turk").

The Finlander, nevertheless, has a claim to a dubious sort of immortality. He was the victim in a brilliant game conceived by supermaster Alexander Alekhine in which the initial irrefutable Rook sacrifice occurred as early as move 13!

In the game here, Szabo (which means "Tailor" in Hungarian) executes a neat job, stitching a straitjacket around his opponent. At move 24 he sews up Black's Rook. "So," mused Szabo (musing in English, to make the point), "this proved a fine victory, thanks to my Finnish."

*Position after 16 . . . BxR

NOTES TO THE GAME

a) 11 NxQP, PxN 12 NxP, RxN 13 BxP, N–QB3 14 BxN, N–B3 15 BxR, QxB leaves Black with excellent counter chances.

b) 12 . . . N–Q2 is indicated.

c) Or 17 . . . P–B3? 18 BxP†, K–R1 19 N–N6! PxN 20 Q–R4 mate.

d) In this position, Black must lose at least the Exchange: e.g., 24 . . . R–Q1 25 B–B7 or 24 . . . R–K1 25 P–Q5.

---

† = check; ‡ = double check; § = dis. check

42

AH SWEET MYSTERY OF NIMZOVICH!

The hypermodern Nimzovich built a fabulous reputation on the eccentricities of his moves. Here he (White) smashes up Behting's Greco Counter, employing not only the well known blockade but also a mysterious Bishop move, which is no mystery at all, after Nimzovich explains it. The game, played at Riga, 1919, begins with 1 P–K4, P–K4 2 N–KB3, P–KB4 3 NxP, Q–B3 4 P–Q4.

Cover scoring table at line indicated. Set up position, make Black's next move (exposing table just enough to read it). Now guess White's 5th move, then expose it. Score par, if move agrees; zero, if not. Make move actually given, Black's reply. Then guess White's next, and so on.

COVER WHITE MOVES
IN TABLE BELOW.   EXPOSE ONE LINE AT A TIME

White Played	Par Score	Black Played	Your Selection for White's move	Your Score
		4 .... P–Q3	....	....
5 N–B4 4		5 .... PxP	....	....
6 N–K3 (a) ..4		6 .... P–B3	....	....
7 B–B4 (b) ..3		7 .... P–Q4	....	....
8 B–N3 3		8 .... B–K3	....	....
9 P–QB4 (c) .5		9 .... Q–B2	....	....
10 Q–K2 4		10 .... N–B3	....	....
11 O–O 4		11 .... B–QN5	....	....
12 B–Q2 4		12 .... BxB	....	....
13 NxB 3		13 .... O–O	....	....
14 P–B4! 5		14 .... PxQBP	....	....
15 N/2xBP 4		15 .... Q–K2	....	....
16 P–B5 5		16 .... B–Q4	....	....
17 NxB 4		17 .... PxN	....	....
18 N–K3 (d) ..4		18 .... Q–Q2*	....	....
19 NxP 8		19 .... NxN	....	....
20 QxP 4		20 .... R–Q1	....	....
21 P–B6 6		21 .... PxP (e)	....	....
22 R–B5 5		22 .... K–R1	....	....
23 RxN 4		23 .... R–K1	....	....
24 RxQ 4		24 .... RxQ	....	....
25 R–Q8† 5		25 .... K–N2	....	....
26 R–N8† 4		26 .... K–R3	....	....
27 R–KB1 4		27 .... Resigns	....	....

Total Score . 100 | Your Percentage .... |

SCALE: 75-100—Excellent; 55-74—Superior; 40-54—Good; 25-39—Fair

43

Notes on NIMZOVICH vs. BEHTING

"Eccentric" Nimzovich starts with the two most conservative moves in the book. Behting counters 3 . . . P–KB4, than which there is no more "eccentric" move today. (It was invented 300 years ago by the first chess analyst, the Calabrian Greco—not to be confused with El Greco, the painter.)

This is the Greco Counter Gambit, whose offshoot, much investigated today by Baltic players, has been dubbed the Latvian Gambit.

Black's difficulties stem from the lazy manner in which he develops (or omits developing) his pieces. At move 19 NxP, the game is theoretically won. The resulting sacrifice is followed by a pin against the Black King which cannot be countered.

The Black setup of two advanced Pawns (blockaded and immobile) and a Knight in the stable as late as move 19 are sure evidence that he has mismanaged the opening.

In any case, Black would have been better off playing 19 . . . N–B3, instead of 19 . . . NxP. Though White would have a Pawn plus, Black would retain some measure of counter-attack.

White's key move came very early: 9 P–QB4.

*Position after 18 . . . Q–Q2

NOTES TO THE GAME

a) Take 4 points for 6 N–QB3 also.

b) Typically Nimzovich. The Bishop can be driven away, but a later thrust will split Black's Pawns and re-activate the piece. Take 3 points for 7 N–QB3 also.

c) The point.

d) The second time the Knight acts as a blockader; but this time also as an aggressor.

e) Or 21 . . . N–B3 22 P–B7†, K–R1 23 BxN, QxB 24 P–B8(Q)†!

---

† = check; ‡ = double check; § = dis. check

44

CHECK TO THE MISERABLE KING !

CHECK, CHECK, the ominous check. It brakes the weak and strong alike. Here, at Berlin, 1920, it is the point in the combination of the game between Reti and Tartakover. Tartakover's counter would have worked — except for a little check. This French Defense begins with 1 P–Q4, P–K3 2 P–K4, P–Q4 3 N–QB3, N–KB3 4 B–N5, PxP 5 NxP, QN–Q2 6 N–KB3.

Cover scoring table at line indicated. Set up position, make Black's next move (exposing table just enough to read it). Now guess White's 7th move, then expose it. Score par if your move agrees; zero, if not. Make move actually given, opponent's reply. Then guess White's next and so on.

COVER WHITE MOVES

IN TABLE BELOW.   **EXPOSE ONE LINE AT A TIME**

White Played	Par Score	Black Played	Your Selection for White's move	Your Score
		6 . . . . B–K2	----------------	--------
7 NxN†	_____ 3	7 . . . . BxN (a)	----------------	--------
8 B–K3	_____ 3	8 . . . . O–O	----------------	--------
9 B–Q3	_____ 3	9 . . . . R–K1	----------------	--------
10 P–B3	_____ 4	10 . . . . P–K4	----------------	--------
11 Q–B2	_____ 4	11 . . . . P–KN3	----------------	--------
12 O–O–O	____ 6	12 . . . . PxP	----------------	--------
13 BxQP	_____ 4	13 . . . . BxB	----------------	--------
14 NxB	_____ 3	14 . . . . N–B4	----------------	--------
15 P–KR4	____ 6	15 . . . . NxB†	----------------	--------
16 RxN (b)	___ 3	16 . . . . P–QB4?(c)	----------------	--------
17 N–N5	_____ 4	17 . . . . Q–R4	----------------	--------
18 N–Q6	_____ 4	18 . . . . R–K2	----------------	--------
19 P–R3	_____ 3	19 . . . . B–N5	----------------	--------
20 P–B3	_____ 3	20 . . . . B–K3	----------------	--------
21 Q–Q2	_____ 3	21 . . . . Q–R3	----------------	--------
22 P–R5	_____ 5	22 . . . . R–Q2	----------------	--------
23 PxP	_____ 3	23 . . . . BPxP	----------------	--------
24 R–K1	_____ 4	24 . . . . B–N6	----------------	--------
25 R–K5!	_____ 6	25 . . . . QR–Q1 *	----------------	--------
26 Q–K3!	_____ 7	26 . . . . QxR? (d)	----------------	--------
27 R–K8† (e)	_ 6	27 . . . . K–N2	----------------	--------
28 QxQ	_____ 4	28 . . . . RxN (f)	----------------	--------
29 RxR	_____ 4	29 . . . . RxQ	----------------	--------
30 RxR	_____ 4	30 . . . . Resigns	----------------	--------

Total Score   100 | Your Percentage _____ |

SCALE: 75-100—Excellent; 55-74—Superior; 40-54—Good; 25-39—Fair

Notes on RETI vs. TARTAKOVER

Reti, in his immortal book, *Masters of the Chessboard*, writes of Tartakover: "We can understand the psychology of the chess-player from the psychology of the man.

"Tartakover knows everything, but he does not play those openings which are deemed the strongest; it gives him pleasure to choose those that are considered weaker, so that he can reveal the shortcomings of the recognized theories wherever that is possible.

"Indeed, he has in this way contributed much to the revision of old dogmas."

Reti (the supposed originator) was a hypermodernist by dedication. Tartakover chose to be a hypermodernist from pure contrariness, mainly because the tenets of this school broke so violently with tradition.

* Position after 25 . . . QR-Q1

NOTES TO THE GAME

a) Better than 7 . . . NxN 8 B-Q3, O-O 9 O-O, P-B4 10 PxP, BxP 11 Q-K2, with attacking prospects for White.

b) 16 QxN is better. White over-rates his chances.

c) Black weakens his Q3 on which White soon anchors.

d) 26 . . . R-KB1 is correct, after which each side will repeat moves.

e) Not 27 QxQ, RxN 28 R-K8†, RxR 29 QxR, R-K8†, and Black wins.

f) If 28 . . . RxR 29 NxR *check*.

†=check; ‡=double check; §=discovered check

A Little Steam for a Long Time Mounts the Pressure

GOTHENBERG (Goteborg), 1920, was the scene of many a battle of the giants. Here the mighty Akiba Rubinstein downs the mighty Geza Maroczy, pressing, pressing, pressing until the total pressure is too much. The opening, a Queen's Gambit Declined, is 1 P–Q4, P–Q4 2 N–KB3, N–KB3 3 P–B4, P–K3 4 N–B3, QN–Q2 5 B–N5, B–K2 6 P–K3, O–O 7 R–B1.

Cover scoring table at line indicated. Set up position, make Black's next move (exposing table just enough to read it). Now guess White's 8th move, then expose it. Score par if your move agrees; zero, if not. Make move actually given, opponent's reply. Then guess White's next and so on.

COVER WHITE MOVES IN TABLE BELOW.

EXPOSE ONE LINE AT A TIME

White Played	Par Score	Black Played	Your Selection for White's move	Your Score
		7 .... R–K1	------------------	-----------
8 Q–B2	3	8 .... PxP (a)	------------------	---------
9 BxP	2	9 .... P–B4	------------------	---------
10 O–O	3	10 .... PxP	------------------	---------
11 NxP	4	11 .... P–QR3	------------------	---------
12 KR–Q1	3	12 .... Q–R4	------------------	---------
13 B–R4	2	13 .... N–K4	------------------	---------
14 B–K2	3	14 .... N–N3	------------------	---------
15 B–N3	2	15 .... P–K4	------------------	---------
16 N–N3	3	16 .... Q–B2	------------------	---------
17 Q–N1	3	17 .... Q–N1	------------------	---------
18 B–B3	4	18 .... Q–R2	------------------	---------
19 N–R5	5	19 .... B–QN5	------------------	---------
20 N–B4	3	20 .... B–Q2	------------------	---------
21 N–Q5	4	21 .... NxN	------------------	---------
22 BxN	2	22 .... B–K3	------------------	---------
23 Q–K4 (b)	2	23 .... BxB	------------------	---------
24 RxB	2	24 .... QR–B1	------------------	---------
25 QR–Q1	3	25 .... B–B1 (c)	------------------	---------
26 P–N3	2	26 .... P–N4	------------------	---------
27 N–Q6 (d)	4	27 .... BxN	------------------	---------
28 RxB	3	28 .... R–B2	------------------	---------
29 P–KR4	6	29 .... P–B3	------------------	---------
30 Q–Q5†	4	30 .... K–R1	------------------	---------
31 P–R5	4	31 .... N–B1	------------------	---------
32 P–R6	4	32 .... N–N3*	------------------	---------
33 Q–K6	7	33 .... R–KB1	---------- ------	---------
34 R–Q7	5	34 .... PxP	------------------	---------
35 B–R4	8	35 .... Resigns (e)	------------------	---------

Total Score 100 | **Your Percentage** ----------------------

SCALE: 75-100—Excellent: 55-74—Superior: 40-54—Good: 25-39—Fair

Notes on RUBINSTEIN vs. MAROCZY

The humorous touch is 17 Q–N1, White's side-step with his Queen, an attacking move which places the Black empress in danger. So, the echo, Black's 17 . . . Q–N1, which, seemingly, places the dark Queen in safety. On the contrary, the Black czarina is as deeply mired as ever.

Then Black wastes more time with Queen moves, attempting to get his Queen Rook posted properly. These adjustments, however, present White with opportunities to occupy strong points, to command files and diagonals.

White's 20 P–KR4 initiates the final windup of a positional attack so well timed that Black, with even material, never finds a chance for counterplay.

*Position after 32 . . . N-N3

NOTES TO THE GAME

a) Contrary to concern for the *tempo*, Black takes without first waiting for White's King Bishop to have moved.

b) White ought to win a Pawn: score five if you chose 23 NxP, NxN 24 BxN, B-N5 25 B-Q4.

c) Not 25 . . . P-B4 26 QxBP, RxN 27 R-Q8, RxR 28 RxR†, followed by 29 Q-K6† and the recovery of the Rook.

d) Not 27 NxP, P-B3 28 R-Q7, QxR. etc.

e) If 35 . . . NxB, 36 Q-K7, etc.

EXCEPTION TO THE RULE

THAT patience is a virtue is so axiomatic as to be platitudinous: that it is so in chess is erratic. Here at Budapest, 1896, Master S. Winawer (Black) certainly bides his good time to build his defenses; for he wishes to build them well. American grandmaster Harry Nelson Pillsbury, however, has other ideas on the subject. Before Winawer can say Jack Robinson, all of the White horses and all of the White men fall upon the poor Black King -- and he can't be put together again. The game begins with 1 P–Q4, P–Q4 2 P–QB4,.P–K3 3 N–QB3.

Cover the scoring table at the line indicated. Set up the position and make Black's next move (exposing the table just enough to be able to read it). Now guess White's fourth move, then expose it. Score par if your move is in agreement; score zero, if not. Make the move actually given, then the opponent's reply. Then guess White's next move, and so on.

COVER WHITE MOVES
IN TABLE BELOW.   EXPOSE ONE LINE AT A TIME

White Played	Par Score	Black Played	Your Selection for White's move	Your Score
		3 . . . . P–QB3	-----------------	--------
4 P–K3	5	4 . . . . N–B3	-----------------	--------
5 N–B3	4	5 . . . . QN–Q2	-----------------	--------
6 B–Q3	4	6 . . . . B–Q3	-----------------	--------
7 O–O	4	7 . . . . O–O	-----------------	--------
8 P–K4	6	8 . . . . PxKP (a)	-----------------	--------
9 NxP	3	9 . . . . NxN	-----------------	--------
10 BxN	3	10 . . . . N–B3	-----------------	--------
11 B–B2	6	11 . . . . P–KR3 (b)	-----------------	--------
12 B–K3	6	12 . . . . R–K1	-----------------	--------
13 Q–Q3	7	13 . . . . Q–B2 (c)	-----------------	--------
14 P–B5 (d)	6	14 . . . . B–B1	-----------------	--------
15 N–K5	6	15 . . . . BxP*	-----------------	--------
16 BxP! (e)	8	16 . . . . BxP (f)	-----------------	--------
17 QxB	6	17 . . . . PxB	-----------------	--------
18 Q–KB4	6	18 . . . . N–Q4 (g)	-----------------	--------
19 QxRP	6	19 . . . . P–B3	-----------------	--------
20 P–B4	8	20 . . . . R–K2	-----------------	--------
21 N–N6	6	21 . . . . Resigns	-----------------	--------

| Total Score 100 | Your Percentage ----------------- | |

SCALE: 75-100—Excellent; 55-74—Superior; 40-54—Good; 25-39—Fair

Notes on PILLSBURY vs. WINAWER

Pillsbury was the foremost advocate of the Queen's Gambit Declined Opening. He refined and sharpened the debut and certain variations are still termed the Pillsbury Attacks. Quick retributions against small inaccuracies in the "Queen's" garnered many victories for the American ace.

Black's 13 . . . Q–B2 is mistimed, allowing White to dominate the center with a Knight. Black's attempt to undermine the cavalry is defeated by a sharp retort from which there is no recovery. Black never solved the problem of what to do with his Queen Bishop. Minus this development he is unable to launch sufficient counter chances.

Noteworthy is the force of White's 8 P–K4. Probably, all Black's troubles stem from his second-best answer to this move: 8 . . . PxKP.

Position after 15 . . . BxP

NOTES TO THE GAME

a) Better is 8 . . . PxBP, drawing White's pieces away from the center.

b) Part of Winawer's patience, perhaps, and preventing White inroads.

c) Sauce for the goose, etc. If White is to attack KR7, why not Black?

d) Well, here's one reason why not.

e) An unexpected counter-stroke.

f) If 16 . . . PxB, White has 17 Q-N3†, followed by 18 N-N6†, and Black's Queen goes.

g) If 18 . . . K-N2, see note "f."

† = check; ‡ = dbl. check; § = dis. ch.

NO MERE AUTOMATONS THESE!

Here Dr. Max Euwe (White) battles the mighty Akiba Rubinstein to a brilliant triumph at Mahrisch–Ostrau, 1923, beginning with 1 N–KB3, P–Q4 2 P–Q4, N–KB3 3 P–K3, P–K3 4 B–Q3, P–B4 5 P–QN3, N–B3 6 O–O, B–Q3 7 B–N2, O–O 8 P–QR3.

Cover scoring table as indicated. Set up position, make Black's move (exposing table just enough to read it). Guess White's 7th move, then expose it. Score par if your move agrees; zero, if not. Make moves actually given, opponent's reply. Then guess White's next, and so on.

COVER WHITE MOVES
IN TABLE BELOW.   EXPOSE ONE LINE AT A TIME

White Played	Par Score	Black Played	Your Selection for White's move	Your Score
		8 .... P–QN3	....	....
9 N–K5	2	9 .... B–N2	....	....
10 N–Q2	2	10 .... Q–K2	....	....
11 P–KB4	4	11 .... KR–Q1	....	....
12 R–B3	4	12 .... N–K5!	....	....
13 R–R3 (a)	4	13 .... P–B4	....	....
14 BxN	4	14 .... QPxB	....	....
15 Q–R5	4	15 .... BxN (b)	....	....
16 QxP†	3	16 .... K–B2	....	....
17 BPxB (c)	2	17 .... R–R1	....	....
18 QxR	2	18 .... RxQ	....	....
19 RxR	2	19 .... B–R3	....	....
20 N–B1	2	20 .... Q–Q2? (d)	....	....
21 R–Q1!	5	21 .... NxKP	....	....
22 F–Q5!	5	22 .... N–N5	....	....
23 PxP†	4	23 .... QxP	....	....
24 R/8–Q8	4	24 .... B–N4	....	....
25 P–B4	2	25 .... B–K1	....	....
26 R/1–Q5	4	26 .... P–B5!	....	....
27 P–R3	4	27 .... PxP	....	....
28 N–N3	4	28 .... P–K7	....	....
29 NxP	2	29 .... N–K6	....	....
30 R–N5	4	30 .... P–N3	....	....
31 N–B4!!	7	31 .... Q–K2 ☆	....	....
32 RxNP	4	32 .... N–B4 (e)	....	....
33 R–B6†	4	33 .... K–N1	....	....
34 RxB†	4	34 .... QxR	....	....
35 RxN	4	35 .... P–K6	....	....
36 R–N5†	2	36 .... K–R2	....	....
37 R–R5†	2	37 .... Resigns (f)	....	....

Total Score   100   Your Percentage ....   _____

SCALE: 75-100—Excellent; 55-74—Superior; 40-54—Good; 25-39—Fair

Notes on EUWE vs. RUBINSTEIN

If Euwe's finishing technique and steadiness of nerves had equaled his chess knowledge he could have stayed champion of the world. His great fault, which prevented him from taking many first prizes in tournaments, was to let down after his deep strategy and forceful tactics had achieved a much superior position from the opening and middle game.

Frequently, for no apparent reason but sheer chess "weariness," Euwe has let many a win slip away. This characteristic was notable and grievous when Euwe participated in the five-player tournament in 1948 to decide the world title. The other contestants were Botvinnik (the eventual winner), Smyslov, Keres, and Reshevsky.

When Euwe is at his best, his game is a harmonious evolution of winning strategy in the opening, middle and end game.

Position after 31 . . . Q-K2

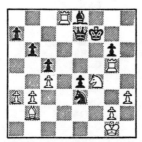

NOTES TO THE GAME

a) On 13 QNxN, PxN 14 BxP, NxN 15 BxP†, K-B1, Black takes the lead.

b) Not 15 . . . P-N3 16 NxNP. Nor 15 . . . P-KR3 16 NxN, BxN 17 PxP, with strong pressure against Black's KN2.

c) Not 17 Q-R5† as White is out a piece after 17 . . . P-N3.

d) Better is 20 . . . BxN, followed by 21 . . . Q-N4.

e) If 32 . . . QxR, White has a quick mate!

f) For White easily forces a win after 37 . . . K-N1 38 R-R8† and 39 RxQ.

52

NO MOOT QUESTION HERE!

The pesky P–KR3 has usurped more than its fair share of space in sundry discourses on the relative merits of tactical plays. It is good; it is indifferent; it is bad — all depending on the specific position. Here, at Hanover, 1926, in the game between Meister Mieses (White) and Gottschall, it is profoundly bad. And twenty-seven moves after it is made comes the denouement. The Opening, a Vienna, begins with 1 P–K4, P–K4 2 N–QB3, N–KB3 3 B–B4, B–B4 4 P–Q3, P–KR3 5 P–B4!

Cover scoring table at line indicated. Set up position, make Black's next move (exposing table just enough to read it). Now guess White's 6th move, then expose it. Score par if your move agrees; zero, if not. Make move actually given, opponent's reply. Then guess White's next and so on.

COVER WHITE MOVES
IN TABLE BELOW. EXPOSE ONE LINE AT A TIME

White Played	Par Score	Black Played	Your Selection for White's move	Your Score
		5 .... P–Q3	-----------------	---------
6 P–B5! _____	5	6 .... P–B3	-----------------	---------
7 Q–B3 (a) __	4	7 .... P–QN4	-----------------	---------
8 B–N3 _____	2	8 .... Q–N3	-----------------	---------
9 KN–K2 ____	3	9 .... P–QR4	-----------------	---------
10 P–QR3 ____	2	10 .... P–R5	-----------------	---------
11 B–R2 _____	2	11 .... B–N2	-----------------	---------
12 P–KN4 (b)	5	12 .... QN–Q2	-----------------	---------
13 N–N3 _____	4	13 .... K–K2 (c)	-----------------	---------
14 P–R4 _____	4	14 .... QR–KB1	-----------------	---------
15 P–N5 _____	4	15 .... N–K1	-----------------	---------
16 P–B6† _____	6	16 .... PxP	-----------------	---------
17 N–B5† _____	5	17 .... K–Q1	-----------------	---------
18 NxRP ____	4	18 .... R–R2	-----------------	---------
19 Q–B5 _____	4	19 .... R–N2	-----------------	---------
20 NxP† (d) __	6	20 .... R/BxN	-----------------	---------
21 BxR _____	2	21 .... RxB	-----------------	---------
22 P–N6 _____	4	22 .... R–N2	-----------------	---------
23 P–R5 _____	4	23 .... B–B1	-----------------	---------
24 P–R6 _____	4	24 .... R–N1	-----------------	---------
25 P–R7 _____	4	25 .... R–R1	-----------------	---------
26 B–R6 _____	4	26 .... N–B1*	-----------------	---------
27 P–N7 _____	5	27 .... NxP	-----------------	---------
28 QxP† _____	4	28 .... K—B2	-----------------	---------
29 QxN† _____	3	29 .... B–Q2	-----------------	---------
30 QxR _____	3	30 .... B–N8	-----------------	---------
31 QxN (e) ___	3	31 .... Resigns	-----------------	---------

Total Score 100 Your Percentage ---------------------

SCALE: 75-100—Excellent; 55-74—Superior; 40-54—Good; 25-39—Fair

Notes on MIESES vs. GOTTSCHALL

Black's aim in this and all openings of a similar nature (the Giuoco Piano and the King's Gambit) is to get in a timely . . . P–Q4. Failing to do so, White will then have a lasting initiative.

Black's Pawn maneuvers on the Queen-side so early are unconvincing. White's King Bishop is only driven to a better square without any benefit on Black's part.

White's sacrifice of two pieces for a Rook is sound because of his subsequent two connected passed Pawns; and Black's stifled piece setup is wholly inadequate for a defense.

One can say unequivocally that Black's needless 4 . . . P–KR3 is the foundation for his demise. The move created two evils: a bad hole and a good target.

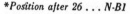

*Position after 26 . . . N-B1

NOTES TO THE GAME

a) White prevents Black's natural counter of 7 . . . P-Q4.

b) Here White initiates a powerful King-side demonstration.

c) If Black castles long, he loses the King Bishop Pawn.

d) Interesting and correct.

e) Meister Mieses was awarded the brilliancy prize for this game.

---

† = check; ‡ = dbl. check; § = dis. ch.

THE BIGGER THEY COME, THE HARDER THEY FALL!

The tragi-comical note of the following game points a moral. It is merely that, when you've got your opponent down, put him out. Harry Nelson Pillsbury, one of the American giants of chess, comes out swinging. He lands a right, he lands a left, and another and another. But one is on his own kisser—and he's out. Jackson Showalter of Kentucky leads off in this Petroff Defense at Cambridge Springs, 1904: 1 P-K4, P-K4 2 N-KB3, N-KB3 3 NxP, P-Q3 4 N-KB3, NxP 5 P-Q4, P-Q4 6 B-Q3.

Cover scoring table as indicated. Set up position, make Black's move (exposing table just enough to read it). Guess White's 7th move, then expose it. Score par if your move agrees; zero, if not. Make moves actually given, opponent's reply. Then guess White's next, and so on.

COVER WHITE MOVES
IN TABLE BELOW.   EXPOSE ONE LINE AT A TIME

White Played	Par Score	Black Played	Your Selection for White's move	Your Score
		6 . . . . B–K2		
7 O–O	4	7 . . . . N–QB3		
8 R–K1	4	8 . . . . B–KN5		
9 P–B3	4	9 . . . . P–B4		
10 QN–Q2	4	10 . . . . O–O		
11 Q–N3	4	11 . . . . K–R1		
12 QxNP (a)	1	12 . . . . R–B3 (b)		
13 Q–N3	4	13 . . . . R–N3		
14 K–B1	4	14 . . . . R–QN1		
15 Q–B2	4	15 . . . . B–Q3		
16 P–KR3	3	16 . . . . B–R4		
17 P–R3	3	17 . . . . Q–B3		
18 N–K5 (c)	2	18 . . . . NxN? (d)		
19 PxN	3	19 . . . . QxP? (e)		
20 N–B3	4	20 . . . . BxN		
21 PxB	3	21 . . . . Q–R7 (f)		
22 B–K3	4	22 . . . . QxRP†		
23 K–K2	3	23 . . . . N–N4		
24 BxBP	4	24 . . . . QxP†		
25 K–Q2	3	25 . . . . N–K5†		
26 BxN	4	26 . . . . PxB		
27 QR–Q1	4	27 . . . . B–B5		
28 K–B1	4	28 . . . . R–N7		
29 Q–Q2	4	29 . . . . BxB		
30 RxB (g)	6	30 . . . . QxP *		
31 R–K2 (h)	13	31 . . . . Resigns		

| Total Score | 100 | Your Percentage | | |

SCALE: 75-100—Excellent; 55-74—Superior; 40-54—Good; 25-39—Fair

55

Notes on SHOWALTER vs. PILLSBURY

The opening was a favorite with Pillsbury. Black's motif is to establish a central Knight and White would be well advised to try to undermine it, rather than achieving the win of a Queen-side Pawn.

This dubious sally presents Black with at least four *tempos*, enabling him to build up an overwhelming position against the White King.

White's side-step, K–B1, hardly slows up the assault. Black, however, fails to make the most of his opportunities. Nevertheless, after the end game is reached, Black is a Pawn plus with a far superior position and will win with proper care.

Was it carelessness, an optical illusion or clock trouble that impelled Black to play . . . QxP, thereby winning a Pawn and losing the game?

*Position after 30 . . . QxP

a) White's strategy to gain a Pawn at the expense of position is highly speculative.

b) Threatening 13 . . . N-N5, followed by 14 . . . R-QN3, winning the Queen.

c) Offering the ill-gotten gains for freedom.

d) The mechanical move, 18 . . . BxN, followed by 19 . . . Q-N4, leaves White defenseless.

e) Again, 19 . . . Q-N4.

f) 21 . . . N-N6† is a killer.

g) Did Pillsbury expect 30 QxB?

h) White wins a Rook, or mates.

TEMPORAL RELATIVITY

In one sense, time is relatively unimportant in chess. It matters but little whether a game is won in forty moves or twenty — so long as it is won. Here, in the Abbazia Gambit Tournament of 1912, R. Reti (Black) acquires a winning position. He ought to consolidate. Instead, he forces, creates weaknesses in his own camp, and R. Spielmann takes over. The opening, a King's Gambit, begins with 1 P–K4, P–K4 2 P–KB4, PxP 3 N–KB3, N–KB3 4 N–B3.

Cover scoring table at line indicated. Set up position, make Black's next move (exposing table just enough to read it). Now guess White's 5th move, then expose it. Score par, if move agrees; zero, if not. Make move actually given, Black's reply. Then guess White's next, and so on.

COVER WHITE MOVES IN TABLE BELOW.   **EXPOSE ONE LINE AT A TIME**

White Played	Par Score	Black Played	Your Selection for White's move	Your Score
		4 .... P–Q4	....	....
5 P–K5	3	5 .... N–K5	....	....
6 B–K2	3	6 .... N–B3	....	....
7 P–Q3	4	7 .... NxN	....	....
8 PxN	1	8 .... P–KN4 (a)	....	....
9 O–O	3	9 .... R–KN1 (b)	....	....
10 P–Q4	4	10 .... P–N5	....	....
11 N–K1	3	11 .... P–B6	....	....
12 B–Q3	3	12 .... Q–R5	....	....
13 B–KB4 (c) .	6	13 .... PxP	....	....
14 NxP	1	14 .... Q–R4	....	.....
15 R–N1	5	15 .... N–Q1	....	....
16 P–B4 (d) ..	7	16 .... B–K3	....	....
17 N–K3	5	17 .... PxP	....	....
18 B–K4 (e) ..	7	18 .... P–QB3	....	....
19 P–Q5	7	19 .... B–QB4	....	....
20 K–R1 (f) ..	6	20 .... BxN	....	....
21 PxB	4	21 .... NxP	....	....
22 BxB	2	22 .... QxKP	....	....
23 BxKRP	5	23 .... R–R1 *	....	....
24 RxBP (g) .	9	24 .... R–Q1 (h)	....	....
25 QxP	5	25 .... QxB	....	....
26 B–N6	7	26 .... Resigns	....	....
Total Score	100	Your Percentage ---------------------		

SCALE: 75-100—Excellent; 55-74—Superior; 40-54—Good; 25-39—Fair

Notes on SPIELMANN vs. RETI

Here Black's too-ambitious attack rebounded. To be sure, some lines were opened against the White King, but these very lines in the end left the Black monarch unguarded.

Black is in the greater danger throughout the complications because of the separation of his Rooks. At first glance, the diagram may give the impression that the White King's position is the most precarious. The opposite is true.

Perhaps Reti was impelled to rush things too soon for psychological reasons. Each game in the Abbazia tournament was a gambit game, in which, according to the rules, the player of the Black side had to accept the gambit Pawn.

Wide-open slam-bang and slash was the atmosphere of such a tourney. Reti's style (after he had developed one later) became a very different thing of discreet mystification; and even today the so-called Reti Systems are often misunderstood.

* Position after 23 ... R–R1

NOTES TO THE GAME

(a) Black is now a solid Pawn plus.

(b) Black ought not attack. 9 . . . B-K3 consolidates.

(c) Reducing Black's offensive to nil.

(d) White takes the initiative.

(e) White preserves his force to harass the enemy King.

(f) If 20 PxB, NxP 21 Q-K2, NxB 22 RxN, QxKP 23 QR-KB1, Q-B6, the issue is in doubt.

(g) The unexpected resource.

(h) If 24 . . . KxR, Black is soon mated.

---

† = check; ‡ = double check; § = dis. check

FILES ON PARADE

On a single track with a concealed purpose, Grandmaster Spielmann (White) lines up, apparently to no avail. But where there's a Spielmann, there's a way. And a file opens as if by magic. Rubinstein takes the brunt of the batteries in the Hungarian Defense at Carlsbad, 1907 with 1 P–K4, P–K4 2 N–KB3, N–QB3 3 B–B4, B–K2 4 N–B3, N–B3 5 P–Q3, P–Q3 6 P–KR3, N–QR4 7 B–N3.

Cover scoring table at line indicated. Set up position, make Black's next move (exposing table just enough to read it). Now guess White's 8th move, then expose it. Score par, if move agrees; zero, if not. Make move actually given, Black's reply. Then guess White's next, and so on.

COVER WHITE MOVES
IN TABLE BELOW.   EXPOSE ONE LINE AT A TIME

White Played	Par Score	Black Played	Your Selection for White's move	Your Score
		7 .... NxB	....	....
8 RPxN	 2	8 .... O–O	....	....
9 O–O	 3	9 .... P–B3	....	....
10 N–K2	 4	10 .... Q–B2	....	....
11 P–KN4	 4	11 .... P–Q4	....	....
12 N–N3	 3	12 .... R–K1	....	....
13 Q–K2	 3	13 .... PxP	....	....
14 PxP	 3	14 .... P–KN3	....	....
15 B–N5	 3	15 .... B–K3	....	....
16 Q–K3	 3	16 .... P–QR3	....	....
17 N–K1	 4	17 .... N–Q2	....	....
18 BxB	 2	18 .... RxB	....	....
19 Q–R6	 5	19 .... R–Q1	....	....
20 K–R2	 4	20 .... P–B3	....	....
21 N–Q3	 3	21 .... R–N2	....	....
22 R–KN1	 3	22 .... N–B1*	....	....
23 N–KB5 (a)	6	23 .... BxN (b)	....	....
24 NPxB	 3	24 .... R–Q5 (c)	....	....
25 R–N4	 3	25 .... QR–Q2	....	....
26 N–B5	 3	26 .... QR–K2	....	....
27 QR–KN1	.. 3	27 .... Q–Q3	....	....
28 N–Q3	 2	28 .... P–R4	....	....
29 P–R4	 4	29 .... Q–B2	....	....
30 R/4–N3	... 4	30 .... R/K–B2	....	....
31 P–KB4 (d)	5	31 .... Q–K2	....	....
32 PxKP	 3	32 ... . BPxP	....	....
33 R–N5	 3	33 .... N–Q2	....	....
34 PxP	 3	34 .... PxP	....	....
35 RxNP	 2	35 .... N–B3	....	....
36 R/1–N5	 4	36 .... NxP	....	....
37 R–R5	 4	37 .... Resigns (e)	....	....

| Total Score | 100 | Your Percentage _____ | | |

SCALE: 75-100—Excellent; 55-74—Superior; 40-54—Good; 25-39—Fair

Notes on SPIELMANN vs. RUBINSTEIN

This game illustrates the chess-playing style of the early years of the century. The motifs are clear, clean-cut. After the first ten moves the strategy for both sides has been formulated.

Spielmann aims to plant a Knight at his KB5. Black's 14 . . . P–KN4, far from hindering the assault, on the contrary helps White in developing his breakthrough.

Rubinstein is nailed down to defending and has no time to create a counter-attack on the Queen's wing. With the advent of each White attacker, Black is able to plant a defender. But at last White's Pawn widens the breakthrough to victory.

Modern theory regards the opening styles of the "romantics" as too easily refutable. These days, both White and Black, from the first moves, employ unbalanced, dissembling setups. Present-day players must have an immense lot of book knowledge to prevail.

*Position after 22 . . . N–B1

Notes to the Game

a) The tamest game, even the Hungarian Defense, is given the Spielmann touch.

b) On 23 . . . PxN 24 NPxP, the simultaneous attack on Bishop and King Bishop Pawn in conjunction with the open King Knight file is in White's favor.

c) Time lost — though Black is condemned to marking time, anyway.

d) Every White man now exerts its power in the assault.

e) It's soon mate.

† = check; ‡ = double check; § = dis. check

UNBALANCING FACTORS

When an opening leads to an unbalanced position, as here, there is only one way to determine the advantage! Look for the names of the players! In this case, Botvinnik (White) has the advantage. He has a good Knight, bad Pawns and Botvinnik on his side. The scene is Moscow, 1940, and Loewenfisch is the victim. The game, an English Opening, begins: 1 P–QB4, P–K4 2 N–QB3, N–KB3 3 N–B3, N–B3 4 P–Q4, PxP 5 NxP.

Cover scoring table at line indicated. Set up position, make Black's next move (exposing table just enough to read it). Now guess White's 6th move, then expose it. Score par, if move agrees; zero, if not. Make move actually given, Black's reply. Then guess White's next, and so on.

COVER WHITE MOVES

IN TABLE BELOW.   EXPOSE ONE LINE AT A TIME

White Played	Par Score	Black Played	Your Selection for White's move	Your Score
		5 .... B–N5	....	....
6 B–N5	 4	6 .... P–KR3	....	....
7 B–R4	 3	7 .... BxN†	....	....
8 PxB	 1	8 .... N–K4 (a)	....	....
9 P–K3	 3	9 .... N–N3	....	....
10 B–N3	 3	10 .... N–K5	....	....
11 Q–B2	 4	11 .... NxB (b)	....	....
12 RPxN	 3	12 .... P–Q3	....	....
13 P–B4	 6	13 .... Q–K2	....	....
14 K–B2	 6	14 .... N–B1 (c)	....	....
15 P–QB5!	... 8	15 .... PxP? (d)	....	. .....
16 B–N5† *	... 5	16 .... N–Q2 (e)	....	....
17 N–B5	 4	17 .... Q–B3	....	....
18 QR–Q1	 5	18 .... P–KN3	....	..... .
19 NxP	 5	19 .... R–B1	....	....
20 P–N4	 4	20 .... P–R3	....	....
21 P–N5	 4	21 .... Q–K3	....	....
22 B–K2	 5	22 .... N–N3	....	....
23 N–N4	 5	23 .... K–K2	....	..... .
24 N–B6	 5	24 .... Q–B3	....	......
25 R–R7	 6	25 .... B–B4	....	....
26 P–K4	 5	26 .... B–K3	....	....
27 P–B5	 6	27 .... Resigns (f)	....	....
Total Score	100	Your Percentage _____		_____

SCALE: 75-100—Excellent; 55-74—Superior; 40-54—Good; 25-39—Fair

Notes on BOTVINNIK vs. LOEWENFISCH

The opening is a favorite with Botvinnik. It lends itself to transpositions, can take on the character of a White Queen's Pawn game or, as in the case here, one in which White plays a sort of Sicilian Defense with a move ahead.

Botvinnik, a most eclectic player, prefers unbalanced positions from the very first move.

After 12 . . . P–Q3, an oft-repeated position arises. But now Botvinnik carries through an original line of attack: 13 P–B4!—the beginning of a peculiar Pawn structure in the center with the White King on B2.

Loewenfisch doesn't expect any disturbing reply and calmly plays 13 . . . Q–K2. (The correct maneuver is . . . N–B1–K3.) In answer to 14 K–B2, N–B1, there follows another subtle move, 15 P–QB5 (clearing the diagonal for White Bishop). After 15 . . . PxP 16 B–N5 ch, Black is unexpectedly in a tight squeeze. His resistance lasts only 11 moves more.

* Position after 16 B–N5†

NOTES TO THE GAME

(a) Two Bishops and White's dominating Knight versus a ragged Pawn position is the issue.

(b) Now it is the dominating Knight versus the ragged Pawns.

(c) 14 . . . B–Q2 is better.

(d) Again 15 . . . B-Q2.

(e) 18 . . . P-B3 19 NxP. Or 18 . . . B-Q2 19 N-B5, Q-B3 20 Q-K4†, followed by QxP.

(f) 27 . . . PxP 28 PxP, B-Q4 29 P-B4, BxNP 30 R-R2 traps the Bishop.

† = check; ‡ = double check; § = dis. check

NOTHING NEW, ETC.

Ancient history is Lasker's defeat of Tarrasch in a match in 1908. Not so hoary, however, is Black's treatment of the French Defense, in vogue today and considered a current predilection. Interesting is Lasker's (White's) interstitial maneuvering on both wings, provoking and exploiting weaknesses. The game begins with 1 P–K4, P–K3 2 P–Q4, P–Q4 3 N–QB3, N–KB3 4 B–N5.

Cover scoring table at line indicated. Set up position, make Black's next move (exposing table just enough to read it). Now guess White's 5th move, then expose it. Score par, if move agrees; zero, if not. Make move actually given, Black's reply. Then *guess* White's next, and so on.

COVER WHITE MOVES IN TABLE BELOW. **EXPOSE ONE LINE AT A TIME**

White Played	Par Score	Black Played	Your Selection for White's move	Your Score
		4 .... B–N5 (a)	....	....
5 PxP	3	5 .... QxP	....	....
6 N–B3	3	6 .... P–B4 (b)	....	....
7 BxN	4	7 .... PxB	....	....
8 Q–Q2	4	8 .... BxN	....	....
9 QxB	3	9 .... N–Q2	....	....
10 R–Q1 (c) ..	4	10 .... KR–N1	....	....
11 PxP	3	11 .... QxBP	....	....
12 Q–Q2	4	12 .... Q–N3	....	....
13 P–B3	3	13 .... P–QR3	....	....
14 Q–B2	4	14 .... P–B4	....	....
15 P–KN3	5	15 .... N–B4	....	....
16 B–N2	4	16 .... Q–B2	....	....
17 Q–K2	4	17 .... P–QN4 (d)	....	....
18 O–O	4	18 .... B–N2	....	....
19 P–B4	5	19 .... P–N5	....	....
20 Q–Q2	5	20 .... R–N1	....	....
21 Q–R6	5	21 .... BxN	....	....
22 BxB	3	22 .... Q–K4 (e)	....	....
23 KR–K1	5	23 .... QxP*	....	....
24 Q–B4!	5	24 .... R–QB1	....	....
25 Q–Q6	6	25 .... P–B3	....	....
26 B–R5†	4	26 .... R–N3	....	....
27 BxR†	3	27 .... PxB	....	....
28 RxP†	7	28 .... Resigns	....	....

Total Score 100 | Your Percentage .... | ——————

SCALE: 75-100—Excellent; 55-74—Superior; 40-54—Good; 25-39—Fair

Notes on LASKER vs. TARRASCH

Black's downfall stems from his King position, which has remained uncomfortable all through the game—a hovering danger in many variations of the French Defense. The game is an ideal example of a contest between two styles: the freewheeling method of the pragmatist Lasker, author of *Common Sense in Chess*, versus the somewhat "theoretical" sorties of Tarrasch.

En passant, if we may veer a bit from the French Defense to another debut, the Two Knights' Defense, after the moves 1 P–K4, P–K4 2 N–KB3, N–QB3 3 B–B4, N–B3 4 N–KN5, Tarrasch maintained that White's last (4 N–KN5) was "a coffeehouse mistake." But, according to Euwe, this is the most promising continuation at White's command. Thus, practice negates theory.

Tarrasch, nevertheless, was always a stern competitor whose theories gained him many top prizes. What really broke his spirit in the end was his non-admittance to the entry list of the great New York Tournament of 1924. Lasker, who had been chosen to compete, had been wrangling for a higher retainer. The committee warned him that, if he didn't accept the offer, Tarrasch would be his replacement. Lasker quickly came to terms.

*Position after 23 ... QxP

NOTES TO THE GAME

a) Contemporary players think this is a modern idea.

b) Easier is 6 . . . N–K5 7 B–Q2, BxN 8 PxB. NxB.

c) 10 O–O–O is better: e.g., 10 . . . PxP 11 NxP, QxRP 12 B–B4, Q–R8† 13 K–Q2, Q–R5 14 B–N5, and White wins the Queen.

d) Now the Pawn structure on both wings is weak.

e) A transparent trap (23 QxRP??).

---

† = check; ‡ = double check; § = dis. check

NIMZOVICH THE CLASSICIST

The designation, Nimzovich the hypermodern, conjures up the slow, tedious, close, positional struggle for the center and a long drawn out game, finally ending in a state of attrition. Here, at Kecskemet, 1927, versus Gilg (Black), it is definitely not so. In truly classical style, the great master takes his opponent in tow in short order. The opening, a Sicilian, begins with 1 P–K4, P–QB4 2 N–KB3, N–QB3 3 B–N5.

Cover scoring table at line indicated. Set up position, make Black's next move (exposing table just enough to read it). Now guess White's 4th move, then expose it. Score par, if move agrees; zero, if not. Make move actually given, Black's reply. Then guess White's next, and so on.

COVER WHITE MOVES

IN TABLE BELOW.   EXPOSE ONE LINE AT A TIME

White Played	Par Score	Black Played	Your Selection for White's move	Your Score
		3 . . . . Q–B2	----------------	--------
4 P–B3	4	4 . . . . P–QR3	----------------	--------
5 B–R4	3	5 . . . . N–B3	----------------	--------
6 Q–K2	4	6 . . . . P–K4	----------------	--------
7 O–O	4	7 . . . . B–K2	----------------	--------
8 P–Q4	4	8 . . . . BPxP (a)	----------------	--------
9 PxP	4	9 . . . . NxQP	----------------	--------
10 NxN	4	10 . . . . PxN	----------------	--------
11 P–K5	6	11 . . . . P–Q6 (b)	----------------	--------
12 Q–K3	6	12 . . . . N–Q4	----------------	--------
13 Q–N3	6	13 . . . . P–KN3	----------------	--------
14 B–N3	6	14 . . . . N–N5*	----------------	--------
15 BxP†	10	15 . . . . K–Q1 (c)	----------------	--------
16 B–R6 (d)	9	16 . . . . N–B7	----------------	--------
17 N–B3	7	17 . . . . N–Q5 (e)	----------------	--------
18 QxQP	6	18 . . . . QxP	----------------	--------
19 KR–K1	8	19 . . . . Q–B3	----------------	--------
20 RxB	9	20 . . . . Resigns (f)	----------------	--------

| Total Score | 100 | Your Percentage | ---------------- | -------- |

SCALE: 75-100—Excellent; 55-74—Superior; 40-54—Good; 25-39—Fair

Notes on NIMZOVICH vs. GILG

White's 3 B–N5, for many years, was considered one of Nimzovich's "jokes" in opening play. However, in the last decade the idea has been used so successfully by Rossolimo, the French-American master, that the debut has been named the Rossolimo Variation.

Black's greedy winning of a Pawn leaves him with holes all over the board and a very backward development. White's 11 P–K5 already underlies his winning method, as it is the prelude for a possible P–K6, in a sub-variation which would win the Black Queen.

Especially time-wasting are Black's Knight maneuvers to reach QB7, filching a Rook. But after arriving at the desired square, the Black horse wheels about and tries to retrieve the disaster. Too late.

Comment: Nimzovich: Very sharp; Gilg: An indifferent E for effort.

*Position after 14 . . . N–N5

NOTES TO THE GAME

a) Black succumbs to the temptation of a Pawn. 8 . . . P-Q3 is correct.

b) On 11 . . . N-Q4 12 P-K6, PxP 13 QxKP, N-N3 14 B-KN5, Q-Q1 15 BxB, NxB 16 Q-N3, QxB 17 QxN, White stands better.

c) Or 15 . . . KxB 16 P-K6†!

d) Way on the King-side, the Bishop eyes the Queen-side (see note e).

e) Or 17 . . . NxR 18 N-Q5, Q-B3 19 B-K3, P-Q3 20 B-N6†, K-Q2 21 P-K6 mate.

f) 20 . . . KxR 21 N-Q5† or 20 . . . QxR 21 QxN.

---

† = check; ‡ = dbl. check; § = dis. check

SPIELMANN OUTSPIELED

The task of the brilliant player is to be brilliant. And the psychological onus falls on him. Hence, he seeks unusual, unbalanced positions as a medium for his talent. Here at Ostend, 1908, master of sacrifices, R. Spielmann (Black) unbalances the opening, and the game collapses—on him—due to von Scheve's nimble management. The opening, a Ruy Lopez, begins 1 P–K4, P–K4 2 N–KB3, N–QB3 3 B–N5.

Cover scoring table at line indicated. Set up position, make Black's next move (exposing table just enough to read it). Now guess White's 4th move, then expose it. Score par, if move agrees; zero, if not. Make move actually given, Black's reply. Then guess White's next, and so on.

COVER WHITE MOVES
IN TABLE BELOW.   EXPOSE ONE LINE AT A TIME

White Played	Par Score	Black Played	Your Selection for White's move	Your Score
		3 .... N–Q5	---------------	--------
4 NxN	3	4 .... PxN	---------------	--------
5 P–Q3	3	5 .... P–QB3	---------------	--------
6 B–QB4	3	6 .... N–K2	---------------	--------
7 Q–B3	4	7 .... P–Q4 (a)	---------------	--------
8 PxP	3	8 .... PxP	---------------	--------
9 B–N3	3	9 .... B–K3	---------------	--------
10 B–N5	3	10 .... P–KR3	---------------	--------
11 B–KB4	3	11 .... N–B3	---------------	--------
12 N–Q2	3	12 .... B–QN5	---------------	--------
13 P–QR3	3	13 .... B–R4	---------------	--------
14 O–O–O	4	14 .... QR–B1	---------------	--------
15 Q–N3	4	15 .... Q–B3	---------------	--------
16 P–KR4	4	16 .... O–O	---------------	--------
17 N–B3	3	17 .... KR–K1	---------------	--------
18 K–N1	3	18 .... R–K2?*	---------------	--------
19 B–N5 (b)	7	19 .... PxB	---------------	--------
20 PxP	4	20 .... Q–B4	---------------	--------
21 R–R5 (c)	6	21 .... Q–N3 (d)	---------------	--------
22 QR–R1	5	22 .... P–B4	---------------	--------
23 R–R8†	4	23 .... K–B2	---------------	--------
24 RxR	4	24 .... BxR	---------------	--------
25 BxP†	3	25 .... R–K3 (e)	---------------	--------
26 R–R8	5	26 .... K–K2 (f)	---------------	--------
27 RxB	3	27 .... R–K7	---------------	--------
28 BxN	3	28 .... PxB	---------------	--------
29 Q–N8	4	29 .... B–N3	---------------	--------
30 Q–N7†	3	30 .... Resigns	---------------	--------

Total Score   100 | Your Percentage --------------------

SCALE: 75-100—Excellent; 55-74—Superior; 40-54—Good; 25-39—Fair

Notes on VON SCHEVE vs. SPIELMANN

In a try to cash in on the inexperience of his opponent, Spielmann adopts an off-beat defense, the Bird Variation of the Spanish Game. The idea was invented (not patented) by the eccentric English bookkeeper and chess master, H. S. Bird, who also gave his name to another opening: 1 P–KB4, called "the Bird," which was frequently adopted by Nimzovich and Tartakover. A player who desires a change of pace may employ it without jeopardizing his initiative.

However, the Bird Variation in the Ruy Lopez (as played here) is not to be recommended. The move 3 . . . N–Q5 violates a basic principle: "Don't move a piece twice in the opening" (unless your opponent has offered you, through a violation of principle or because of a blunder, an opportunity for an immediate tactical advantage in material and space).

White's 16 P–KR4 was the lever which projected the victory. And the winning method was only accelerated by a previous move of Black 10 . . . P–KR3. Another illustration of the old saw: "Don't push Pawns at random in front of a castled King."

*Position after 18 . . . R–K2?

NOTES TO THE GAME

a) From now on, Black can anticipate a weak end-game position.

b) An unusual sacrifice violently to expose the enemy King.

c) The point, permitting the doubling of the Rooks and other tactical threats.

d) If 21 . . . P-KN3, White wins with 22 R-R8†, KxR 23 Q-R4†, followed by 24 R-R1.

e) If 25 . . . B-K3? 26 BxN and 27 N-K5†.

f) Black has to avoid 27 Q-Q6 which soon leads to mate.

† = check; ‡ = dbl. check; § = dis. check

WHAT'S IN A NAME?

The designation, "drawing master," for Carl Schlechter can be taken with a grain of salt. As witness how here as White at the Master Tournament of Ostend, 1906, he lights into Amos Burn with a sacrificial combination which makes the rafters ring. The opening is a staid, old Queen's Gambit Declined. It begins with these moves: 1 P–Q4, P–Q4 2 P–QB4, P–K3 3 N–QB3, N–KB3 4 N–B3, QN–Q2 5 B–N5, B–K2 6 P–K3, and nothing so far suggests fireworks to come.

Cover scoring table at line indicated. Set up position, make Black's next move (exposing table just enough to read it). Now guess White's 7th move, then expose it. Score par, if move agrees; zero, if not. Make move actually given, Black's reply. Then guess White's next, and so on.

COVER WHITE MOVES
IN TABLE BELOW.   EXPOSE ONE LINE AT A TIME

White Played	Par Score	Black Played	Your Selection for White's move	Your Score
		6 .... O–O	....	....
7 Q–B2	 2	7 .... P–QN3 (a)	....	....
8 PxP	 6	8 .... PxP	....	....
9 B–Q3	 3	9 .... B–N2	....	....
10 O–O	 3	10 .... P–B4	....	....
11 PxP	 6	11 .... PxP (b)	....	....
12 QR–Q1	 3	12 .... P–N3 (c)	....	....
13 B–N5!	 6	13 .... K–N2	....	....
14 P–K4	,.... 6	14 .... P–Q5 *	....	....
15 NxP	 8	15 .... PxN	....	....
16 RxP	 3	16 .... B–B1 (d)	....	....
17 Q–Q2	 5	17 .... P–QR3	....	....
18 B–B6	 5	18 .... R–R2	....	....
19 B–R6†	 5	19 .... K–N1	....	....
20 P–K5	 6	20 .... NxP (e)	....	....
21 RxQ	 4	21 .... RxR	....	....
22 B–Q5	 5	22 .... R/2–Q2	....	....
23 Q–K2	 5	23 .... RxB	....	....
24 NxR	 4	24 .... RxN	....	....
25 R–Q1	 4	25 .... B–KN5? (f)	....	....
26 RxR	 7	26 .... BxQ	....	....
27 RxN	 4	27 .... Resigns	....	....

Total Score   100 | Your Percentage _____   _____

SCALE: 75-100—Excellent; 55-74—Superior; 40-54—Good; 25-39—Fair

Notes on SCHLECHTER vs. BURN

Too readily, thought the experts, Schlechter accepted draws when he had the superior position. "He is too kindhearted." The comment is perhaps exaggerated. He was known, however, as the "drawing master." In a certain sense, this is commendatory. Schlechter was a tough man to beat outright.

On the other hand, the title "drawing master" was also a belittling one. There is justification for Schlechter's actions:

In Schlechter's match with Emanuel Lasker for the world title, after nine rounds Schlechter was a point ahead. All he needed to become champion was to draw the final game. He played to win, mismanaged the ending, and lost. The score was tied. Instead of the game being drawn, it was the match. Lasker retained his title. And Schlechter his.

*Position after 14 . . . P–Q5

NOTES TO THE GAME

a) This variation was in popular favor at the time.

b) Black's move is probably best, but it does result in hanging Pawns.

c) Here, though, 12 P-KR3 is better.

d) Actually, 16 . . . Q-N3 puts up more resistance: 17 RxN, NxR 18 BxB nets White two Pawns and strong position for the Exchange.

e) As good as any.

f) But this move hastens the end.

---

† = check; ‡ = double check; § = dis. check

70

SANS VOIR ET SANS REPROCHE

Skill at blindfold play is an acquired talent. The present record is forty-five games simultaneously. Here world champion, Wilhelm Steinitz, shows how it was done during a blindfold seance in Scotland in 1867 against one of six opponents. P. Scott is the victim in this French Defense, beginning with 1 P–K4, P–K3 2 P–Q4, P–Q4 3 N–QB3, B–N5 4 PxP, BxN† 5 PxB.

Cover scoring table at line indicated. Set up position, make Black's next move (exposing table just enough to read it). Now guess White's 6th move, then expose it. Score par if your move agrees; zero, if not. Make move actually given, opponent's reply. Then guess White's next, and so on.

**COVER WHITE MOVES
IN TABLE BELOW.**   EXPOSE ONE LINE AT A TIME

White Played	Par Score	Black Played	Your Selection for White's move	Your Score
		5 .... PxP	-----------------	--------
6 N–KB3 _____ 3		6 .... Q–K2† (a)	-----------------	--------.
7 B–K2 _____ 4		7 .... N–KB3	-----------------	-------.-
8 P–QR4 (b) 7		8 .... QN–Q2	-----------------	--------
9 B–QR3 _____ 7		9 .... P–B4	-----------------	--------
10 O–O _____ 3		10 .... O–O	-----------------	--------
11 R–K1 _____ 4		11 .... P–QN3	-----------------	--------
12 P–B4 _____ 5		12 ..., B–N2	-----------------	--------
13 PxQP _____ 6		13 .... BxP	-----------------	--------
14 B–N5 _____ 6		14 .... Q–Q3	-----------------	--------
15 N–K5 (c) _ 5		15 .... QR–Q1 (d)	-----------------	--------
16 NxN _____ 8		16 .... NxN	-----------------	--------
17 BxN _____ 7		17 .... RxB (e) *	-----------------	--------
18 PxP _____ 6		18 .... PxP	-----------------	--------
19 P–QB4 _____ 6		19 .... BxBP	-----------------	--------
20 QxQ _____ 6		20 .... RxQ	-----------------	--------
21 BxP _____ 6		21 .... R–K3	-----------------	--------
22 RxR _____ 3		22 .... PxR	-----------------	--------
23 BxR _____ 3		23 .... KxB	-----------------	--------
24 R–QB1 _____ 3		24 .... B–Q4	-----------------	--------
25 R–B8† _____ 2		25 .... Resigns	-----------------	--------

Total Score   100 | Your Percentage ------------------

SCALE: 75-100—Excellent; 55-74—Superior; 40-54—Good; 25-39—Fair

71

Notes on STEINITZ vs. SCOTT

Doubled Pawns are usually to be avoided. In this game, however, White's pair on the QB file are used with sharp effect on 12 P–B4 and 19 P–B4. Black's weak points, his QB4 and Q4, are undermined.

The possession of the diagonal QR3–KB8 by the White Bishop, the control of the open King's file and the half-open Queen's file allow White to act forcefully against the awkward positions of Black's Queen and King Rook.

At the time, Steinitz's blindfold feat was considered remarkable. Philidor was the first to play without sight of board or men: against 2 experts. So astonishing was the event that its authenticity was notarized afterward.

After Steinitz: Blackburne, Alekhine, Koltanowski and Najdorf excelled in blindfold play. Najdorf's record at São Paulo topped them all when he played 45 simultaneously without sight of board and men.

Position after 17 . . . RxB

NOTES TO THE GAME

a) An unnecessary check, exposing Black's Queen to future harassment.

b) White establishes a vantage point at QR3 from which to molest the Queen.

c) Now White threatens to win a Pawn by 16 NxN, NxN 17 BxN. QxB 18 PxP.

d) The wrong Rook.

e) Better is 17 . . , QxB 18 PxP, Q–B3; for 19 PxP is met by 19 . . . BxP with many complications. Now the Exchange goes lost.

---

†=check; ‡=double check; §=discovered check

THE PLAY'S THE THING

"One move after another" has been used to mean a game bereft of ideas. This game, however, is one good move after another — nothing startling, just good. And the goodness thereof is more than enough to tell. Hungarian grandmaster L. Szabo (White) does in his countryman G. Barcza, Budapest, 1946 in this Gruenfeld which begins: 1 P-Q4, N-KB3 2 P-QB4, P-KN3 3 N-QB3, P-Q4 4 N-B3, B-N2 5 Q-N3, PxP 6 QxBP.

Cover scoring table at line indicated. Set up position, make Black's next move (exposing table just enough to read it). Now guess White's 7th move, then expose it. Score par if your move agrees; zero, if not. Make move actually given, opponent's reply. Then guess White's next, and so on.

COVER WHITE MOVES IN TABLE BELOW.   **EXPOSE ONE LINE AT A TIME**

White Played	Par Score	Black Played	Your Selection for White's move	Your Score
		6 .... P-B3	----------------	--------
7 P-K4	4	7 .. . B-K3	----------------	--------
8 Q-Q3	2	8 .... N-R3	----------------	--------
9 B-K2	2	9 .... B-N5	----------------	--------
10 B-K3	2	10,.... Q-R4	----------------	--------
11 O-O	2	11 .... R-Q1	----------------	--------
12 P-QR3 (a)	4	12 .... O-O	----------------	--------
13 P-N4	4	13 .... Q-B2	----------------	--------
14 QR-B1	3	14 .... Q-N1	----------------	--------
15 Q-B2	3	15 .... N-B2	----------------	--------
16 P-R3	4	16 .... BxN	----------------	--------
17 BxB	2	17 .... P-K4 (b)	----------------	--------
18 PxP	3	18 .... N-Q2	----------------	--------
19 B-K2 (c)	5	19 .... NxP	----------------	--------
20 P-B4	4	20 .... N-Q2	----------------	--------
21 P-K5	5	21 .... N-K3	----------------	--------
22 B-B4	4	22 .... N-N3	----------------	--------
23 KBxN	5	23 .... PxB	----------------	--------
24 B-B5	4	24 .... R-B2	----------------	--------
25 N-K4 (d)	5	25 .... N-Q4 *	----------------	--------
26 N-N5	4	26 .... RxP	----------------	--------
27 NxKP	6	27 .... RxR†	----------------	--------
28 RxR	2	28 .... R-K1	----------------	--------
29 NxB	5	29 .... KxN	----------------	--------
30 Q-B2	6	30 .... Q-B2	----------------	--------
31 P-K6!	5	31 .... P-KN4	----------------	--------
32 Q-Q4†	5	32 .... Resigns (e)	----------------	--------

| Total Score | 100 | Your Percentage | ---------------- | -------- |

SCALE: 75-100—Excellent; 55-74—Superior; 40-54—Good; 25-39—Fair

Notes on SZABO vs. BARCZA

Black loses this game because of his isolated King's Pawn and his inability to retain his King Bishop for defensive purposes. Black's capture of White's King Bishop Pawn (seemingly compensation for the loss of his own King Pawn) is a boomerang shot:

Thereby the KB file is opened and since it is White who commands it, Black rapidly becomes saddled with troubles he cannot overcome.

Szabo, whose inherent chess talent is equal to the best, is handicapped by unsteady nerves at the decisive moments. During the interzonal tourney at Saltsjobaden, 1948, it appeared that Szabo was going to win the contest. He was leading up to two rounds before the end. He had clear wins in both his games against Stoltz and Lundin, but could only acquire a half point from both, and so had to content himself with second place below Bronstein.

Position after 25 . . . N-Q4

NOTES TO THE GAME

a) Preventing 12 . . . N-B4, to be met by 13 P-QN4 and the gain of a piece.

b) Not a real sacrifice as Black must recover the Pawn. His contention of the center, however, opens the game wide, and White's better development then tells.

c) This key move retains the Bishop, makes way for a center Pawn majority advance.

d) Now it looks as though the Knight is headed for Q6; but, actually, it creates havoc at N5.

e) After 33 R-B7(†), it's soon over.

74

MAKING IT A "GOOD INDIAN"

Among the current crop of masters, Dutchman J. H. Donner is a constant threat. Here at Wageningen, 1957, as White, he rips into the Nimzo-Indian set up by Roumanian Dr. O. Trojanescu with a vengeance and comes through in brilliant style. The opening begins with 1 P–Q4, N–KB3 2 P–QB4, P–K3 3 N–QB3, B–N5 4 P–K3.

Cover scoring table at line indicated. Set up position, make Black's next move (exposing table just enough to read it). Now guess White's 5th move, then expose it. Score par, if move agrees; zero, if not. Make move actually given, Black's reply. Then guess White's next, and so on.

EXPOSE ONE LINE AT A TIME

White Played	Par Score	Black Played	Your Selection for White's move	Your Score
		4 .... P–B4	....	....
5 B–Q3 (a)	..3	5 .... O–O	....	....
6 N–B3 (a)	..3	6 .... P–Q4	....	....
7 O–O	3	7 .... N–B3	....	....
8 P–QR3	4	8 .... BPxP	....	....
9 KPxP	4	9 .... PxP	....	....
10 BxP	2	10 .... B–K2 (b)	....	....
11 R–K1	4	11 .... P–QR3	....	....
12 B–R2	5	12 .... P–QN4	....	....
13 P–Q5! (c)	.7	13 .... PxP	....	....
14 NxQP	4	14 .... NxN	....	....
15 QxN (d)	...7	15 .... B–N2	....	....
16 Q–R5	6	16 .... P–N3?	....	....
17 Q–R6	4	17 .... N–Q5	....	....
18 N–N5	5	18 .... BxN	....	....
19 BxB	2	19 .... Q–N3	....	....
20 QR–Q1	4	20 .... QR–B1 (e)	....	....
21 R–K7	5	21 .... Q–Q3	....	....
22 K–R1 (f)	..4	22 .... Q–QB3 *	....	....
23 RxB	7	23 .... N–B4	....	....
24 B–Q5!	6	24 .... Q–B7	....	....
25 R–QB1	5	25 .... Q–K7	....	....
26 BxP†	5	26 .... Resigns	....	....

| Total Score | 100 | Your Percentage _____ | | |

SCALE: 75-100—Excellent; 55-74—Superior; 40-54—Good; 25-39—Fair

Notes on DONNER vs. TROJANESCU

There are no subtleties in this game. Missing are those Pawn-move refinements, seeking to establish a superior Pawn skeleton for the end game. Instead, attack and counter-attack, swashbucklings against Queens and Kings with both opponents in imminent danger.

Parts of the middle-game slam-bang have the character of a prepared study. White's eventual victory is due to the permanent injury in Black's King-side Pawn structure caused by 16 . . . P–N3—another example of the rule: "Never push Pawns in front of the castled King that is under attack except as a last resort."

White's Queen, camping within the enemy fortress, is psychological and material poison. All White's sallies are interlocked with the frightening White lady who, once placed on the dire spot, never budges until Black surrenders. Beware the power of a Donner's woman!

George Treysman, the brilliant New York expert, said: "A piece established on the proper square has its roots in the enemy's body."

*Position after 22 . . . Q–QB3

Notes to the Game

a) Score yourself 3 points also for such reasonable book moves as KN–K2, P–QR3 and even Q–N3.

b) "Book" with minimal initiative for White because of his superior development.

c) Opening lines for a favorable mid-game.

d) The point: if Black exchanges Queens, he loses a piece.

e) 20 . . . Q–QB3 brakes the attack to some extent.

f) To avoid mate (after 22 . . . N–K7†!); but score yourself 5 for the better 22 K–B1.

† = check; ‡ = double check; § = dis. check

76

"SAFETY" PIN CLIPS SWINDLE

Most exciting is the game in which both players are out to beat each other. In this match game of 1909, Marshall (Black) played to win because he was Marshall. And Capablanca played to win because he had to prove that he was Capablanca! The opening, a Ruy Lopez, begins with 1 P-K4, P-K4 2 N-KB3, N-QB3 3 B-N5, P-Q3 4 O-O, P-QR3 5 BxN†, PxB 6 P-Q4.

Cover scoring table at line indicated. Set up position, make Black's next move (exposing table just enough to read it). Now guess White's 7th move, then expose it. Score par if your move agrees; zero, if not. Make move actually given, opponent's reply. Then guess White's next, and so on.

**COVER WHITE MOVES
IN TABLE BELOW.**   **EXPOSE ONE LINE AT A TIME**

White Played	Par Score	Black Played	Your Selection for White's move	Your Score
		6 . . . . PxP	-----------------	--------
7 NxP _____ 2		7 . . . . B-Q2	-----------------	--------
8 R-K1 _____ 2		8 . . . . P-QB4	-----------------	--------
9 N-KB3 _____ 3		9 . . . . B-K2	-----------------	--------
10 N-B3 _____ 2		10 . . . . P-QB3	-----------------	--------
11 B-B4! _____ 3		11 . . . . B-K3	-----------------	--------
12 Q-Q3! _____ 5		12 . . . . N-B3	-----------------	--------
13 QR-Q1 _____ 4		13 . . . . P-Q4	-----------------	--------
14 N-KN5 _____ 5		14 . . . . P-Q5 (a)	-----------------	--------
15 NxB _____ 4		15 . . . . BPxN	-----------------	--------
16 N-R4 _____ 5		16 . . . . Q-R4	-----------------	--------
17 P-QN3 _____ 5		17 . . ... . R-Q1	-----------------	--------
18 N-N2 (b) __ 4		18 . . . . N-R4	-----------------	--------
19 B-K5 _____ 3		19 . . . . O-O	-----------------	--------
20 N-B4 _____ 3		20 . . . . Q-N5	-----------------	--------
21 Q-R3 _____ 4		21 . . . . P-N3	-----------------	--------
22 QxP† _____ 3		22 . . . . R-B2	-----------------	--------
23 P-N4! (c) __ 6		23 . . . . B-R5 *	-----------------	--------
24 PxN _____ 5		24 . . . . BxP†	-----------------	--------
25 K-R1 _____ 3		25 . . . . Q-B6 (d)	-----------------	--------
26 R-K3!! (e) 7		26 . . . . QxBP (f)	-----------------	--------
27 R/3-Q3 ____ 3		27 . . . . Q-K7	-----------------	--------
28 N-Q6 _____ 4		28 . . . . RxN	-----------------	--------
29 BxR _____ 4		29 . . . . B-K8	-----------------	--------
30 Q-K8† _____ 5		30 . . . . K-N2	-----------------	--------
31 P-R6†! ____ 6		31 . . . . Resigns	-----------------	--------
Total Score 100		Your Percentage -----------------		-------

SCALE: 75-100—Excellent; 55-74—Superior; 40-54—Good; 25-39—Fair

Notes on CAPABLANCA vs. MARSHALL

Until he met Capablanca, Marshall's freewheeling, attacking style had wrested victories from many of the top masters. In open-board play Marshall had usually outcombined his opposition.

The Cuban, though, was a dragon of a different color. In this game, Capablanca, maneuvering not to win material but rather to pick flaws in Marshall's Pawn skeleton, outplays the American in the initial stages of a Spanish Debut.

Marshall, with a losing game, conjures up a last-ditch gold-brick scheme which might have paid off against careless defense.

Because of the result of this match, which Capablanca won by 8 games to 1, the Cuban was invited to the San Sebastian tournament where he upset all the favorites and took first prize.

Position after 23 . . . B-R5

Notes to the Game

a) 14 . . . O-O is met by 15 P-K5. The Black Pawns are now weakly disposed.

b) Trap: 18 . . . QxP 19 N-B4, and the Black Queen is lost.

c) Compelling a fierce counter; 23 . . . N-N2 or . . . N-B3 24 BxN permits 25 N-Q6!

d) Typically Marshall, a possible swindle.

e) Typically Capa, reducing something to nothing.

f) If 26 . . . BxR, White has 27 PxP, PxP 28 QxP†, followed by 29 N-Q6.

WHO KILLED COCK ROBIN?

The greatest skill is exhibited in a game in which it is nearly impossible to trace the losing move or plan. Such is this, the sixth game of the Euwe–Bogolyubov match, 1929. The venerable Dr. Max seizes the initiative and hammers the fight out of his game opponent. The Opening: a Queen's Gambit: 1 P-Q4, P-Q4 2 P-QB4, P-K3 3 N-QB3, N-KB3 4 B-N5, QN-Q2 5 P-K3, B-K2 6 N-B3, O-O 7 R-B1, P-QB3 8 B-Q3.

Cover scoring table at line indicated. Set up position, make Black's 8th move (exposing table just enough to read it). Now guess White's 9th, then expose it. Score par if your move agrees; score zero, if not. Make move actually given, opponent's reply. Then guess White's next, and so on.

COVER WHITE MOVES
IN TABLE BELOW. EXPOSE ONE LINE AT A TIME

White Played	Par Score	Black Played	Your Selection for White's move	Your Score
		8 .... P-QR3	----------------	--------
9 PxP	3	9 .... BPxP (a)	----------------	--------
10 O-O	3	10 .... P-QN4	----------------	--------
11 N-K5	4	11 .... NxN	----------------	--------
12 PxN	2	12 .... N-Q2	----------------	--------
13 B-KB4	3	13 .... B-N2	----------------	--------
14 N-K2	4	14 .... Q-N1 (b)	----------------	--------
15 N-Q4 (c)	6	15 .... P-KN3	----------------	--------
16 B-R6	4	16 .... R-QB1 (d)	----------------	--------
17 RxR†	4	17 .... QxR	----------------	--------
18 P-B4	3	18 .... N-B4	----------------	--------
19 P-KN4	5	19 .... NxB	----------------	--------
20 QxN	2	20 .... Q-B5	----------------	--------
21 Q-Q2	4	21 .... B-N5	----------------	--------
22 Q-KB2	4	22 .... Q-Q6	----------------	--------
23 P-B5	4	23 .... Q-K5	----------------	--------
24 Q-N3	4	24 .... KPxP	----------------	--------
25 PxP	3	25 .... B-KB1	----------------	--------
26 BxB	4	26 .... RxB	----------------	--------
27 P-B6	5	27 .... P-KR4	----------------	--------
28 Q-N5	4	28 .... Q-N5†	----------------	--------
29 QxQ	3	29 .... PxQ *	----------------	--------
30 P-K6	6	30 .... K-R2	----------------	--------
31 P-K7	4	31 .... R-K1	----------------	--------
32 R-B1 (e)	5	32 .... K-R3	----------------	--------
33 N-K6	7	33 .... Resigns	----------------	--------

Total Score 100 | Your Percentage -------------------

SCALE: 75-100—Excellent; 55-74—Superior; 40-54—Good; 25-39—Fair

Notes on EUWE vs. BOGOLYUBOV

Euwe, who is above all the master of the opening strategy, achieves a position where his active, centrally dominant Knight is more than equivalent for Black's inactive Bishop, blocked by the Black Pawns.

The doubling of White's Pawns on 12 PxN is in this case strong for White, an exception to the general theory of Pawn structure.

As Black was not able to hinder White's Pawn thrusts on the King-side, White threatened a quick mate with his Queen at KN7. To forestall this, Black must exchange Queens, and leave himself with an inferior end game.

Then, a final tactical Pawn sortie (offering the sacrifice of a Knight), which is irrefutable, seals White's win.

Position after 29 . . . PxQ

NOTES TO THE GAME

a) 7 . . . KPxP leads to the Exchange Variation, a difficult pattern for Black.

b) This play is slow and makes for a laggard development.

c) White defends his King Pawn indirectly, by the counter of 15 . . . NxP 16 Q-R5 or 16 BxP†, followed by Q-R5(†).

d) Now White's attack is irresistible. Better is the offer of the Exchange: 16 . . . NxP.

e) A finesse. Not 32 N-K6 as Black can reply with 32 . . . B-B3.

AN EXCHANGE OF NOTES — OR NOTES TO YOU!

Everything is called a sacrifice these days. When the finale is 1 Q–K8†, RxQ 2 RxR mate, the annotator registers ecstasy on the beautiful Queen sacrifice! To offer material, however, with no return in sight merits the appellation "sacrifice." Here Pinkus (Black) accepts a Pawn with a note on his scoresheet: "You've got to show me," to which Denker replies in like fashion: "I will." The opening, a Queen's Gambit Declined, begins 1 P–Q4, P–Q4 2 P–QB4, P–K3 3 N–QB3, P–QB3 4 P–K4, PxP 5 NxP.

Cover scoring table at line indicated. Set up position, make Black's next move (exposing table just enough to read it). Now guess White's 6th move, then expose it. Score par, if move agrees; zero, if not. Make move actually given, Black's reply. Then guess White's next, and so on.

COVER WHITE MOVES IN TABLE BELOW.

EXPOSE ONE LINE AT A TIME

White Played	Par Score	Black Played	Your Selection for White's move	Your Score
		5 .... B–N5†	....	....
6 N–B3	3	6 .... P–QB4	....	....
7 P–QR3	3	7 .... BxN†	....	....
8 PxB	3	8 .... N–KB3	....	....
9 N–B3	3	9 .... N–B3	....	....
10 B–Q3 (a) ..	5	10 .... PxP	....	....
11 PxP	3	11 .... NxP	....	....
12 O–O	3	12 .... N–B3	....	....
13 B–N2	4	13 .... B–Q2	....	....
14 R–K1	3	14 .... Q–B2	....	....
15 N–K5	4	15 .... P–KR4?	....	....
16 Q–B3	4	16 .... R–R3	....	....
17 Q–N3	4	17 .... NxN (b)	....	....
18 BxN	3	18 .... Q–B4	....	....
19 P–R3 (c) ..	4	19 .... Q–KB1	....	....
20 B–Q6	5	20 .... Q–R1	....	....
21 B–N4	4	21 .... O–O–O	....	....
22 B–R5	5	22 .... P–QN3	....	....
23 P–B5! (d) .	5	23 .... K–N2	....	....
24 PxP	3	24 .... R–QB1 (e)	....	....
25 PxP	3	25 .... N–Q4	....	....
26 Q–Q6	4	26 .... B–B3*	....	....
27 B–R6†	7	27 .... KxB	....	....
28 P–R8(Q)† .	4	28 .... RxQ	....	....
29 QxB†	3	29 .... K–R2 (f)	....	....
30 QR–N1	4	30 .... R–QN1	....	....
31 B–B7	4	31 .... Resigns	....	....
Total Score	100	Your Percentage		————

SCALE: 75-100—Excellent; 55-74—Superior; 40-54—Good; 25-39—Fair

Notes on DENKER vs. PINKUS

Denker is a courageous player who repeatedly disobeys the dictum: "Always sacrifice the other fellow's pieces." He is happiest when offering some Grecian gift to the enemy.

His style has paid off in high circles. He won the U. S. Championship in 1944, nosing out grandmaster Reuben Fine, after having beaten him in their individual game.

Pinkus is a foremost authority on the Two Knights' Defense. Here, he has no chance to entertain his favorite debut, since it is Denker who calls the tune and Pinkus who pays the piper.

Denker's Pawn generosity recompenses him with open lines, two Bishops and a backward Pawn formation of the enemy. Pinkus, unaware of White's strong factors, advances nonchalantly on the King-side, but suddenly his King is dangerously harried. Castling Queen-side, Black is unable to withstand White's sharp and telling play.

Denker's tactics are an example of forceful timing. He employs each piece for its maximum.

*Position after 26 . . . B–B3

NOTES TO THE GAME

a) This is Denker's offer, a sound sacrifice of a Pawn for superior development.

b) Of course not 17 . . . K–B1 18 N–N6†!

c) Apparently, White doesn't want to fool around with 19 QxP, N–N5, etc.

d) Now of course the threat is 24 B–R6 mate.

e) Now, if 24 . . . PxP, 25 BxP!

f) On 29 . . . KxB, White mates in a few moves beginning with 30 R–K4.

---

† = check; ‡ = double check; § = dis. check

THE EXCEPTION TESTS THE RULE

Exceptions to principles are the rule in chess. They are so many, it is necessary to draw a fine line between the principle and the exception. To forfeit castling, for example, was pictured as a bogey to frighten even the initiate. Yet, currently, many masters accept this so-called liability as a matter of course. Here, at the Buenos Aires Team Tournament of 1939, Endzelins (Black) forfeits castling in a French Defense with equanimity. Pleci, however, substantiates the basis of the rule with cogency. The game begins with 1 P–K4, P–K3 2 P–Q4, P–Q4 3 N–Q2.

Cover scoring table at line indicated. Set up position, make Black's next move (exposing table just enough to read it). Now guess White's 4th move, then expose it. Score par, if move agrees; zero, if not. Make move actually given, Black's reply. Then guess White's next, and so on.

**COVER WHITE MOVES
IN TABLE BELOW.**   EXPOSE ONE LINE AT A TIME

White Played	Par Score	Black Played	Your Selection for White's move	Your Score
		3 .... P–QB4	....	....
4 KN–B3 (a)	5	4 .... PxKP	....	....
5 NxP	4	5 .... N–Q2	....	....
6 PxP	4	6 .... NxP	....	....
7 QxQ† (b) ..	4	7 .... KxQ	....	....
8 B–N5†	5	8 .... P–B3	....	....
9 O–O–O†	5	9 .... K–K1	....	....
10 B–N5†	5	10 .... K–B2	....	....
11 R–Q8! (c) .	7	11 .... B–K2 (d) *	....	....
12 N–K5†	9	12 .... PxN	....	....
13 N–Q6†	6	13 .... K–N3	....	....
14 BxB	5	14 .... NxB	....	....
15 RxR (e) ...	4	15 .... P–QR3	....	....
16 B–K2	4	16 .... P–K5	....	....
17 P–KB4	6	17 .... P–N4	....	....
18 R–K8	6	18 .... K–B3	....	....
19 R–B8†	5	19 .... K–N3	....	....
20 P–KR4	6	20 .... B–N2 (f)	....	....
21 P–R5†	5	21 .... K–R3	....	....
22 N–B7 mate	5			

Total Score   100 | **Your Percentage** _____ |

SCALE: 75-100—Excellent; 55-74—Superior; 40-54—Good; 25-39—Fair

Notes on PLECI vs. ENDZELINS

The *tempos* gained by White are crushing. Move 11 R–Q8 is a thrust from which Black cannot recover. The Black King is so confined that it's practically no contest. The remainder of the game is interesting only to illustrate how efficiently White accomplishes his victory. And it is unusual that such a speedy overwhelming of the enemy can be accomplished without Queens on the board.

All Black's troubles stem from his faulty desire to exchange as many pieces as he can right from the start. This idea is particularly erroneous for Black if he chooses the French Defense, an asymmetrical opening. In this case, Black should set up a secure Pawn formation; knowing that if White tries to split the Black skeleton too quickly, the tactic may rebound to Black's favor. Black should play a delaying game. That is the main idea behind 1 . . . P–K3.

By exchanging pairs of center Pawns, Black plays into White's hand. It may be stated, without qualification, that already after 7 QxQ ch, Black cannot recover.

*Position after 11 . . . B–K2

Notes to the Game

a) This is an idea of Alekhine, instead of the more usual 4 KPxP.

b) This wide open position prompts the exchange of Queens whereafter even the minor pieces act powerfully.

c) One *tempo* move follows another, and they are still to come.

d) If 11 . . . PxB or 11 . . . NxN, White has 12 N–K5†, etc.

e) But now White's material superiority decides.

f) Now Black's game collapses at once; but his position was hopeless.

† = check; ‡ = double check; § = dis. check

84

THE QUEEN PAWN HAS MANY FACES

The staid Queen Pawn Opening has its lighter moments. Here at Trenciansk Teplice, 1949, Swedish grandmaster Stahlberg (White) sacrifices more men against Sefc than you will find in the most memorable gambits. When he threatens to give up his Queen, that is the end. The opening begins with 1 P–Q4, P–Q4 2 P–QB4, P–K3 3 N–KB3, N–KB3 4 B–N5.

Cover scoring table at line indicated. Set up position, make Black's next move (exposing table just enough to read it). Now guess White's 5th move, then expose it. Score par, if move agrees; zero, if not. Make move actually given, Black's reply. Then guess White's next, and so on.

COVER WHITE MOVES
IN TABLE BELOW.   EXPOSE ONE LINE AT A TIME

White Played	Par Score	Black Played	Your Selection for White's move	Your Score
		4 . . . . B–N5†	. . . .	. . . .
5 N–B3	 3	5 . . . . PxP	. . . .	. . . .
6 P–K4	 4	6 . . . . P–B4	. . . .	. . . .
7 BxP	 3	7 . . . . PxP	. . . .	. . . .
8 NxP	 3	8 . . . . Q–R4 (a)	. . . .	. . . .
9 BxN	 5	9 . . . . BxN†	. . . .	. . . .
10 PxB	 3	10 . . . . QxP†	. . . .	. . . .
11 K–B1	 3	11 . . . . QxB†	. . . .	. . . .
12 K–N1	 3	12 . . . . N–Q2 (b)	. . . .	. . . .
13 BxP	 4	13 . . . . R–KN1	. . . .	. . . .
14 R–B1	 4	14 . . . . Q–R3	. . . .	. . . .
15 B–R6	 3	15 . . . . N–B3	. . . .	. . . .
16 P–K5!	 5	16 . . . . N–Q4	. . . .	. . . .
17 P–KR4	 5	17 . . . . B–Q2	. . . .	. . . .
18 Q–B2	 6	18 . . . . R–N3	. . . .	. . . .
19 P–R5	 7	19 . . . . R–N5 (c)	. . . .	. . . .
20 QxP	 5	20 . . . . K–K2	. . . .	. . . .
21 R–R4	 6	21 . . . . R/5–N1 (d)	. . . .	. . . .
22 B–N7	 6	22 . . . . Q–R6	. . . .	. . . .
23 B–B6†	 5	23 . . . . K–B1 *	. . . .	. . . .
24 R–B7	 8	24 . . . . NxB (e)	. . . .	. . . .
25 PxN	 4	25 . . . . Q–Q3	. . . .	. . . .
26 P–R6	 5	. . . . Resigns (f)	. . . .	. . . .
Total Score	100	Your Percentage		

SCALE: 75-100—Excellent; 55-74—Superior; 40-54—Good; 25-39—Fair

Notes on STAHLBERG vs. SEFC

Beginning with White's 9 BxN, and from then on in, the attack is carried through fortissimo. Stahlberg offers Sefc almost a fourth part of the White army, squandering his wood to get at the enemy King.

The Swede never lets up. At first Sefc wisely puts aside the temptations proffered by White, but his "cover-up" defense is insufficient. The intensity of Stahlberg's assault terminates in the offer of the Queen, an offer which had been shaped earlier by an innocent-looking Pawn push.

Willy-nilly, Black must gobble the Queen, which proves most indigestible after 26 ... any 27 Q–N7 ch, RxQ 28 PxR ch, K–N1 29 R–N8 mate.

Golembek, the English commentator, wrote: "Nobody among living players has such elegance of style as Stahlberg when playing at his best." Unfortunately, his ill-health has occasionally sapped his stamina, and his inconsistencies have been too frequent for tournament domination.

All too human, Stahlberg!

→Position after 23 ... K–B1

NOTES TO THE GAME

a) The strength of this move is illusory. Superior development favors White with tactical threats.

b) Or else, if 19 ... PxB, 20 R–B1!

c) Or 19 ... RxB? 20 Q–Q2.

d) After 21 ... RxR 22 B–N5†, White soon mates.

e) After 24 ... NxR 25 P–R6, there is no defense against 26 QxR† and 27 P–R7†.

f) Here the threat is 27 Q–N7†.

---

† = check; ‡ = double check; § = dis. check

86

THE FLOHR OF YORE

It is only a score of years ago that Salo Flohr was reckoned to be the leading contender for the world championship. Alekhine, Capablanca and Lasker had all singled him out from the many. Yet he is now relegated to limbo. Among his many fine victories is that against Ravinsky (Black) in the USSR Championship of 1944. A few refinements in the Queen Pawn leave him with a powerful drive: 1 P–Q4, P–Q4 2 P–QB4, P–QB3 3 N–KB3, N–B3 4 N–B3, PxP 5 P–K3, P–QN4 6 P–QR4.

Cover scoring table at line indicated. Set up position, make Black's next move (exposing table just enough to read it). Now guess White's 7th move, then expose it. Score par, if move agrees; zero, if not. Make move actually given, Black's reply. Then guess White's next, and so on.

COVER WHITE MOVES
IN TABLE BELOW.   EXPOSE ONE LINE AT A TIME

White Played	Par Score	Black Played	Your Selection for White's move	Your Score
		6 .... P–N5	....	....
7 N–R2 3		7 .... P–K3	....	....
8 BxP 3		8 .... QN–Q2	....	....
9 O–O 3		9 .... B–N2	....	....
10 Q–K2 3		10 .... P–B4	....	....
11 R–Q1 4		11 .... Q–B2	....	....
12 B–R6 (a) .. 4		12 .... B–Q4	....	....
13 B–Q2 (b) .. 4		13 .... R–QN1	....	....
14 KR–QB1 ... 4		14 .... Q–N3	....	....
15 B–N5 (c) .. 4		15 .... P–QR4	....	....
16 N–K5 3		16 .. : . B–Q3	....	....
17 PxP 3		17 .... BxBP	....	....
18 P–K4 5		18 .... B–N2 (d)	....	....
19 B–N5 4		19 .... B–QB1	....	....
20 B–KB4 4		20 .... R–R1	....	....
21 Q–B2 4		21 .... B–K2*	....	....
22 QxB† 6		22 .... RxQ	....	....
23 RxR† 3		23 .... B–Q1	....	....
24 N–B4 (e) .. 4		24 .... Q–Q5	....	....
25 B–K3 3		25 .... Q–Q6	....	....
26 B–B5 4		26 .... NxP	....	....
27 N–K5 4		27 .... QxB	....	....
28 PxQ 2		28 .... NxN	.. ..	....
29 R–Q1 5		29 .... N–Q2	....	....
30 B–N6 4		30 .... K–K2	....	....
31 BxP! 3		31 .... NxP	....	....
32 RxB 3		32 .... NxR	....	....
33 RxR 2		33 .... P–N6	....	....
34 N–B1 2		34 .... Resigns	....	....

Total Score   100 | Your Percentage ....

SCALE: 75-100—Excellent; 55-74—Superior; 40-54—Good; 25-39—Fair

Notes on FLOHR vs. RAVINSKY ,

During the middle years of Flohr's chess career he is just one of many bright stars in the Soviet galaxy. Flohr, however, started as a youthful prodigy in his native Czechoslovakia.

The peak of this early phase was a drawn match with Mikhail Botvinnik in which the Russian made a last-ditch stand and was able to squeak through for a draw.

During World War II, Flohr fled his native land, became a Soviet citizen and now has an honored post as chess teacher and theoretician in Russia.

The drawback here to Ravinsky's Black defense is that it is "too defensive." Slight inaccuracies, indifferent timings of moves, allow White to tie up the Black phalanx.

Flohr's thrusts follow rapid-fire against the uncomfortable position of the Black King and Queen. Rook-and-Knight shifts, accurately timed, conquer a stubborn defense.

NOTES TO THE GAME
Position in diagram is
after Black's 21 ... B–K2

a) The idea is to split the Queen Knight Pawn from defense by the Queen Rook Pawn.

b) Threatening 14 PxP.

c) Now the pin is predominant.

d) Capture of the King Pawn loses a piece.

e) 24 NxN also wins a piece: 24 . . . NxN 25 B–B7! QxB/2 26 RxQ, BxR 27 R–Q1.

---

† = check; ‡ = double check; § = dis. check

THE PERFECT ANOMALY

LEGEND has Grandmaster Janowski as the disciple of the Two Bishops. At times during his career, he engaged in devious, tortuous maneuvers, merely to preserve his Bishops or to win his opponent's Bishop for a Knight, often to the detriment of his score. Hastings, 1895, however, was another story. There world champion Steinitz (Black) usurped the role which was later to be the Frenchman's, and he came a cropper. This Ruy Lopez (a) began with 1 P-K4, P-K4 2 N-KB3, N-QB3 3 B-N5, P-QR3 4 B-R4.

Cover scoring table at line indicated. Set up position, make Black's next move (exposing table just enough to read it). Now guess White's 5th move, then expose it. Score par if move agrees, zero if not. Make move actually given, opponent's reply. Then guess White's next, and so on.

COVER WHITE MOVES
IN TABLE BELOW.   EXPOSE ONE LINE AT A TIME

White Played	Par Score	Black Played	Your Selection for White's move	Your Score
		.4 .... P-Q3	----------------	--------
5 O-O	3	5 .... KN-K2 (b)	----------------	--------
6 B-N3	4	6 .... N-R4 (c)	----------------	--------
7 P-Q4	4	7 .... PxP	----------------	--------
8 NxP	3	8 .... P-QB4	----------------	--------
9 N-B5	6	9 .... NxN	----------------	--------
10 PxN	3	10 .... NxB	----------------	--------
11 R-K1†	7	11 .... B-K2	----------------	--------
12 P-B6! (d)	7	12 .... PxP (e)	----------------	--------
13 RPxN	3	13 .... P-Q4	----------------	--------
14 Q-R5	6	14 .... Q-Q3	----------------	--------
15 N-B3	4	15 .... B-K3*	----------------	--------
16 N-N5 (f)	6	16 .... Q-B3	----------------	--------
17 RxB!	7	17 .... QxN	----------------	--------
18 B-R6	6	18 .... K-Q1	----------------	--------
19 QxP	5	19 .... R-K1	----------------	--------
20 QR-K1	3	20 .... Q-Q2	----------------	--------
21 B-N7	6	21 .... R-QB1	----------------	--------
22 BxP	5	22 .... BxB	----------------	--------
23 QxB†	5	23 .... K-B2	----------------	--------
24 Q-K5†	5	24 .... Resigns	----------------	--------

| Total Score 100 | Your Percentage ---------------------- | |

SCALE: 75-100—Excellent; 55-74—Superior; 40-54—Good; 25-39—Fair

Notes on JANOWSKI vs. STEINITZ

Janowski's life was a happy one. Chess-playing was both vocation and avocation. He spent his last days among admirers in the New York East-Side coffeehouses where he and the masters Chajes, Jaffe and Jacob Bernstein gave odds ranging from Pawn and Move to full Queen to a regular retinue of clients. The stakes were anything from a thin dime to a five-dollar bill, and always there was betting on the side by kibitzers.

Janowski's weakness as a tournament player (aside from his over-predilection for two Bishops) was a curious one: He hated to end a game even when he had a winning position. He continued to play to the gallery. The "gallery" was his own admiration of his own brilliancies. Lengthening the contest beyond its legitimate span offered opportunities to manufacture a chain of intriguing conceits.

Sometimes, however, these needless prolongations backfired. Janowski's score in tournaments never represented his intrinsic ability. He could topple the best. He would lose to the mediocre. This is the judgment of the players who flourished in his day.

Position after 15 . . . B-K3

NOTES TO THE GAME

a) *MCO*: page 28; column 20.

b) A curiosity of the day, seldom seen now.

c) Black is playing for the minimal advantage of the Bishop over the Knight, but at the expense of time and space.

d) A neat interpolation which breaks up the Black King-side.

e) Not 12 . . . NxR 13 RxB†, K-B1 14 Q-R5, B-K3 15 B-R6! R-N1 16 Q-N5, as there is no adequate defense.

f) Now there is no way to break the subsequent bind.

---

†=check; ‡=double check; §=discovered check

BURN FIDDLES WHILE MARSHALL ROAMS

Here is a rarity—the thematic game. An idea which is sown in the opening play bears its fruit in the middle game. The whole course is a la Marshall—sharp, short and sweet. Amos Burn is Black, and the victim in this Giuoco Piano from the tournament of Ostend, 1905. The game begins with 1 P-K4, P-K4 2 N-KB3, N-QB3 3 B-B4, B-B4 4 P-B3, N-B3 5 P-Q4, PxP 6 PxP.

Cover the scoring table at the line indicated. Set up the position and make Black's next move (exposing the table just enough to read that move). Then guess White's seventh move. Now expose the seventh in the table and score par if your move agrees: score zero, if not. Make the moves as actually played and the opponent's reply. Now guess White's next move and continue the procedure to the finish.

COVER WHITE MOVES

IN TABLE BELOW.   EXPOSE ONE LINE AT A TIME

White Played	Par Score	Black Played	Your Selection for White's move	Your Score
		6 . . . . B-N5†	-----------------	--------
7 K-B1	4	7 . . . . NxKP (a)	-----------------	--------
8 P-Q5	7	8 . . . . N-K2	-----------------	--------
9 Q-Q4	7	9 . . . . N-KB3	-----------------	--------
10 B-KN5	4	10 . . . . N-N3	-----------------	--------
11 QN-Q2	4	11 . . . . P-KR3 (b)	-----------------	--------
12 R-K1†	6	12 . . . . K-B1 (c)	-----------------	--------
13 B-Q3	8	13 . . . . B-K2 (d)	-----------------	--------
14 B/3xN	9	14 . . . . RPxB	-----------------	--------
15 N-K5 (e)	8	15 . . . . PxB	-----------------	--------
16 NxNP†	6	16 . . . . K-B2 *	-----------------	--------
17 RxB†!!	8	17 . . . . KxN	-----------------	--------
18 Q-Q3†	7	18 . . . . K-R3	-----------------	--------
19 P-KR4!	8	19 . . . . P-N5	-----------------	--------
20 P-R5!	8	20 . . . . NxRP	-----------------	--------
21 Q-B5	6	21 . . . . Resigns (f)	-----------------	--------
Total Score	100	Your Percentage	-----------------	-------

SCALE: 75-100—Excellent; 55-74—Superior; 40-54—Good; 25-39—Fair

Notes on MARSHALL vs. BURN

The charming (and most potent) point in the final mating setup is the White Rook *en prise* at K7. This piece, by commanding squares and blocking lines, shuts off all Black defenses against the checkmate.

Another piquant touch in the windup is the strength of White's other Rook—on its original square. Here, the loss of castling did not slow up the White attack, but on the contrary hastened the defeat of Black.

Paradoxically, White's 7 K–B1 is not a defensive move, but is really the first in a far-reaching sequence of forcing tactics against the enemy. It is to be noted that 7 K–B1 accomplishes three things:

1. Places the White King in safety.
2. Prepares a square for the White Queen's Rook.
3. Psychologically lulls Black into the illusion of having, at least, obtained opening equality. This illusion turns into disillusion under Marshall's marshaling of *tempos* and material.

*Position after 16 . . . K-B2

Notes to the Game

a) 6 . . . P-Q4 maintains the better position. The Pawn grab is speculative.

b) 11 . . . B-K2 is indicated. Then White may throw caution to the winds with 12 P—Q6. With two Pawns down, the onus of proving the point rests with White.

c) Not 12 . . . B—K2 13 BxN, PxB 14 QxP.

d) 13 . . . PxB 14 QxB† favors White.

e) The point.

f) 21 . . . P-KN3 22 RxN†, PxR 23 Q-B6 mate.

ONE GOOD SACRIFICE DESERVES ANOTHER

As in the principle of physics, a body in motion tends to remain in motion, so, in chess, one sacrifice engenders others. Here at Moscow, 1943, on his 13th turn, White offers a Pawn. On his 20th, an Exchange goes by the wayside; on 21 a piece; on 26 an Exchange. But it all adds up to checkmate in this fascinating Sicilian between Ravinsky and Panov. The opening, 1 P-K4, P-QB4 2 N-KB3, P-K3 3 P-Q4, PxP 4 NxP, N-KB3 5 N-QB3.

Cover scoring table at line indicated. Set up position, make Black's next move (exposing table just enough to read it). Now *guess* White's 6th move, then expose it. Score par, if move agrees; zero, if not. Make move actually given, Black's reply. Then *guess* White's next, and so on.

COVER WHITE MOVES IN TABLE BELOW.　　　　　　　　**EXPOSE ONE LINE AT A TIME**

White Played	Par Score	Black Played	Your Selection for White's move	Your Score
		5 .... P-Q3	....	....
6 P-KN3	 3	6 .... N-B3	....	....
7 B-N2	 2	7 .... B-Q2	....	....
8 O-O	 2	8 .... P-QR3	....	....
9 B-K3	 2	9 .... R-B1	....	....
10 Q-K2	 2	10 .... P-QN4	....	....
11 P-QR3	 2	11 .... N-K4	....	....
12 QR-Q1	 2	12 .... N-B5	....	....
13 B-B1 (a)	.. 2	13 .... NxRP	....	....
14 P-K5	 3	14 .... PxP	....	....
15 N-N6	 3	15 .... Q-B2	....	....
16 NxKP	 2	16 .... N-B5	....	....
17 NxB	 2	17 .... NxN	....	....
18 N-Q5	 3	18 .... Q-R2	....	....
19 N-B4	 5	19 .... N/5-K4	....	....
20 RxN	 6	20 .... NxR	....	....
21 NxP	 6	21 .... PxN	....	....
22 QxP†	 2	22 .... B-K2 (b)	....	....
23 R-K1	 4	23 .... Q-B4	....	....
24 P-QN4!! (c)	5	24 .... N-B1 (d)	....	....
25 Q-N4	 3	25 .... Q-B6　*	....	....
26 RxB†	 6	26 .... KxR	....	....
27 B-N5†	 4	27 .... K-Q3 (e)	....	....
28 Q-Q1†	 4	28 .... K-B2	....	....
29 B-B4†	 3	29 .... K-N3	....	....
30 Q-Q6†	 3	30 .... K-R2	....	....
31 Q-K7†	 3	31 .... R-B2	....	....
32 BxR	 3	32 .... Q-R8†	....	....
33 B-B1	 1	33 .... N-N3	....	....
34 Q-B5†	 3	34 .... K-N2	....	....
35 B-R5	 5	35 .... R-KB1	....	....
36 Q-N6†	 4	36 .... Resigns	....	....

Total Score . 100 | **Your Percentage** .... _____
SCALE: 75-100—Excellent; 55-74—Superior; 40-54—Good; 25-39—Fair

Notes on RAVINSKY vs. PANOV

White's strategy is a long-range one. It is based on a fianchetto of the King's Bishop, usually a favored idea on the Black-side of this opening.

Black's ill-considered Pawn-win maneuver on the Queen-side delays his castling and allows White to break the center. With well-timed threats White opens the board, raking the Black King's terrain with long-sweeping Bishops and Queen.

Black, practically speaking, is playing the game three pieces down; his King Bishop and the two Rooks hardly enter the fray. White's offer of material can hardly be refused. Black's attempt to escape his King into the corner is doomed because of the premature advance of his Queen-side Pawns.

Panov, who has written a book on the openings, does not follow his own good theoretical advice: "Do not make a committed deployment until all the pieces are developed."

White's star move is 14 P–K5.

*Position after 25 . . . Q–B6

NOTES TO THE GAME

a) Here White offers a Pawn to get up an attack.

b) Or 22 . . . K–Q1 23 B–N5†, K–B2 24 Q–B6†, K–N1 25 B–B4†, R–B2 26 BxR†, QxB 27 Q–R8 mate.

c) So as to try for B–N5.

d) Here 24 QxNP is better, with a view to giving up the Queen.

e) On 27 . . . K–K1, White has 28 Q–K2†, K–B2 29 B–Q5†, K–N3 30 Q–K4†, KxB 31 Q–B4†, K–R4 32 B–B7† and Q–R4 mate.

† = check; ‡ = double check; § = dis. check

WHITE MAGIC

ALMOST ANYBODY can turn a vastly superior position into a win. It takes an artist, however, to conjure something out of nothing. Here former world champion, Dr. Max Euwe, nurses a small positional advantage into a violent breakthrough on the King's wing. C. Carls is his victim (Black) at The Hague, 1928, in this Reti Opening. The game begins with 1 N-KB3, N-KB3 2 P-B4, P-B4 3 P-KN3, N-B3 4 B-N2, P-KN3 5 P-N3.

Cover scoring table at line indicated. Set up position, make Black's next move (exposing table just enough to read that move). Guess White's sixth move. Now expose next line; score par, if your move agrees; score zero, if not. Make move given, then guess White's next, and so on.

COVER WHITE MOVES

IN TABLE BELOW.   EXPOSE ONE LINE AT A TIME

White Played	Par Score	Black Played	Your Selection for White's move	Your Score
		5 .... B-N2	------------------	--------
6 B-N2 _____	2	6 .... P-Q3	------------------	--------
7 P-Q4 _____	4	7 .... PxP	------------------	--------
8 NxP _____	3	8 .... B-Q2	------------------	--------
9 O-O _____	3	9 .... O-O	------------------	--------
10 N-QB3 _____	3	10 .... NxN?	------------------	--------
11 QxN _____	2	11 .... B-B3	------------------	--------
12 N-Q5! (a) _	6	12 .... N-R4	------------------	--------
13 Q-Q2 _____	2	13 .... BxB	------------------	--------
14 QxB _____	2	14 .... BxN	------------------	--------
15 BxB _____	3	15 .... Q-N3? (b)	------------------	--------
16 KR-Q1 ____	4	16 .... N-B3	------------------	--------
17 B-B3 _____	4	17 .... KR-B1 (c)	------------------	--------
18 R-Q4 _____	4	18 .... P-QR4	------------------	--------
19 QR-Q1 _____	5	19 .... R-B2 (d)	------------------	--------
20 P-KR4 _____	6	20 .... P-R4*	------------------	--------
21 RxP! _____	8	21 .... PxR	------------------	--------
22 QxN _____	2	22 .... R-KB1 (e)	------------------	--------
23 RxP ___-___	2	23 .... Q-B4	------------------	--------
24 B-Q5 _____	5	24 .... K-R2	------------------	--------
25 P-KN4!! (f)	9	25 .... Q-R6	------------------	--------
26 PxP _____	4	26 .... Q-B8†	------------------	--------
27 K-R2 _____	2	27 .... Q-R3	------------------	--------
28 BxP! _____	6	28 .... Q-N2	------------------	--------
29 PxP† _____	5	29 .... K-R1	------------------	--------
30 Q-N5 _____	4	30 .... Resigns	------------------	--------

| Total Score | 100 | Your Percentage ------------------ | | ---------- |

SCALE: 75-100—Excellent; 55-74—Superior; 40-54—Good; 25-39—Fair

Notes on EUWE vs. CARLS

Only after most of the pieces are exchanged does Black's game fall apart. Black became saddled with permanent weakness on the dark squares guarding his King. After White's sacrifice, his dominant Bishop and a Pawn breakthrough which could not be prevented secured the win.

Euwe was always particularly sharp against weaker players. Employing maneuvers which at first glance seem superficial and drawish, he was able to create end-game superiority.

Underlying these apparently aimless, listless swaps is a keen appraisal of minor-piece advantage in the end game; Euwe was an expert in the motif of Bishop versus Knight and vice versa.

Position after 20 . . . P-R4

a) Inducing further exchanges with a view of slightly weakening Black's King position.

b) Black ought to aim for an eventual . . . P-QN4; hence, the text is out of order.

c) Threatening 18 . . . RxP.

d) 19 . . . R-B4 gives a better defensive post. Next move, it is imperative.

e) 22 . . . R-Q2 fails after 23 B-Q5 which threatens 24 QxNP!.

f) Shattering the defensive barrier. 25 . . . PxP loses to 26 P-R5.

A DAY OF REST

ONE of the greatest chess tournaments was Nottingham, 1936, with Alekhine, Lasker, Capablanca, Botvinnik, Reshevsky, Fine and Keres. For them, a day of rest was a game with one of the masters. Here Fine (White) enjoys a day of rest against Winter in a Slav Defense, which starts: 1 P-Q4, P-Q4 2 P-QB4, P-QB3 3 N-KB3, N-KB3 4 P-K3, B-B4 5 N-B3.

Cover scoring table at line indicated. Set up position, make Black's 5th move (exposing table just enough to read it). Guess White's move, then expose next line. Score par if your move agrees; if not, zero. Make move given, opponent's reply. Guess White's next, and so on to end.

COVER WHITE MOVES
IN TABLE BELOW.   EXPOSE ONE LINE AT A TIME

White Played	Par Score	Black Played	Your Selection for White's move	Your Score
		5 .... P-K3	-----------------	--------
6 N-KR4	4	6 .... B-K5	-----------------	--------
7 P-B3	3	7 .... B-N3	-----------------	--------
8 NxB	2	8 .... RPxN	-----------------	--------
9 P-KN3	3	9 .... B-Q3	-----------------	--------
10 P-B4 (a)	3	10 .... N-K5	-----------------	--------
11 NxN	3	11 .... PxN	-----------------	--------
12 B-Q2	2	12 .... Q-K2	-----------------	--------
13 P-QR3 (b)	5	13 .... N-Q2	-----------------	--------
14 Q-N3	4	14 .... R-QN1	-----------------	--------
15 Q-R4	4	15 .... P-R3	-----------------	--------
16 B-K2	2	16 .... P-KN4 (c)	-----------------	--------
17 O-O-O	4	17 .... P-KB4	-----------------	--------
18 PxP	2	18 .... QxP	-----------------	--------
19 P-B5	4	19 .... B-B2*	-----------------	--------
20 BxP (d)	7	20 .... PxB	-----------------	--------
21 QxBP	5	21 .... K-Q1	-----------------	--------
22 QxKP	3	22 .... Q-B3	-----------------	--------
23 Q-Q5	3	23 .... K-K2	-----------------	--------
24 B-N4	4	24 .... KR-QB1	-----------------	--------
25 K-N1	4	25 .... N-B1	-----------------	--------
26 P-KN4	5	26 .... P-R4	-----------------	--------
27 B-B3	4	27 .... P-N3	-----------------	--------
28 PxP	3	28 .... QxBP	-----------------	--------
29 Q-B4	3	29 .... N-K3	-----------------	--------
30 KR-B1	3	30 .... Q-R4	-----------------	--------
31 P-Q5	5	31 .... NxP	-----------------	--------
32 P-Q6†	6	32 .... Resigns (e)	-----------------	--------
Total Score	100	Your Percentage	-----------------	

SCALE: 75-100—Excellent; 55-74—Superior; 40-54—Good; 25-39—Fair

Notes on FINE vs. WINTER

Fine undoubtedly possessed a great natural gift for chess. He had a sound appreciation of opening problems and his games often gave evidence of an outstanding mathematical power of calculation.

Fine had outpointed Reshevsky in the great international tournaments where both participated. But in the United States Reshevsky proved his superior and was able to defend his championship against Fine's challenges.

The Slav Defense is played to solve the development of Black's Queen Bishop plausibly. As played here, White obtains a two-Bishop edge over Bishop and Knight, and barring any counter by Black, White's game is potentially the more threatening.

Position after 19 ... B-B2

Notes to the Game

a) Threat was 10 . . . BxP†. If 10 B-N2, RxP, followed by 11 . . . BxP†.

b) White prevents an exchange by 13 . . . B-N5 and at the same time discourages the break 13 . . . P-QB4: e.g., 14 PxP, BxQBP 15 P-QN4.

c) Premature. 16 O-O is better.

d) A surprise move. White gets three Pawns plus a strong attack for his piece.

e) Enough. is enough. An excellent game.

WHEN KNIGHTS AND CHESSPLAYERS WERE BOLD

In days of old, debuts were bold, and interesting games were produced. Here Schiffers (White) explores the staid Giuoco Piano and injects rich blood into its lines to make Harmonist bow in relatively few moves. The quiet 26th is a work of art. The game begins with 1 P–K4, P–K4 2 N–KB3, N–QB3 3 B–B4, B–B4 4 P–B3.

Cover scoring table at line indicated. Set up position, make Black's next move (exposing table just enough to read it). Now guess White's 5th move, then expose it. Score par, if move agrees; zero, if not. Make move actually given, Black's reply. Then guess White's next, and so on.

COVER WHITE MOVES
IN TABLE BELOW.   EXPOSE ONE LINE AT A TIME

White Played	Par Score	Black Played	Your Selection for White's move	Your Score
		4 .... N–B3	-----------------	--------
5 P–Q4 (a)	3	5 .... PxP	-----------------	--------
6 PxP	2	6 .... B–N5†	-----------------	--------
7 B–Q2 (b)	2	7 .... BxB†	-----------------	--------
8 QNxB	2	8 .... P–Q4	-----------------	--------
9 PxP	2	9 .... KNxP (c)	-----------------	--------
10 Q–N3	5	10 .... QN–K2 (d)	-----------------	-------
11 O–O	2	11 .... O–O	-----------------	--------
12 R–K1	3	12 .... P–QB3	-----------------	--------
13 P–QR4	5	13 .... Q–B2	-----------------	--------
14 QR–B1 (e)	5	14 .... N–B5	-----------------	--------
15 N–N5	4	15 .... N/2–N3 ❋	-----------------	--------
16 R–K8	7	16 .... RxR	-----------------	--------
17 BxP†	3	17 .... K–R1 (f)	-----------------	--------
18 BxR	4	18 .... N–K7†	-----------------	--------
19 K–R1	3	19 .... NxR	-----------------	--------
20 N–B7†	4	20 .... K–N1	-----------------	--------
21 N–R6‡	4	21 .... K–B1	-----------------	---------
22 Q–N8†	5	22 .... K–K2	-----------------	--------
23 BxN	5	23 .... PxB	-----------------	--------
24 QxP†	6	24 .... K–Q1	-----------------	--------
25 Q–B8†	6	25 .... K–Q2	-----------------	--------
26 N–K4	8	26 .... Q–Q1	-----------------	--------
27 Q–Q6†	5	27 .... K–K1	-----------------	--------
28 N–B6†	5	28 .... Resigns	-----------------	--------
Total Score 100		Your Percentage ----------------		

SCALE: 75-100—Excellent; 55-74—Superior; 40-54—Good; 25-39—Fair

Notes on SCHIFFERS vs. HARMONIST

Here Black, Harmonist, starts jigging willy-nilly to Schiffers' tune. Black's 13 ... Q–B2 is inaccurate, and he should have opposed White's Queen with 13 ... Q–N3. In a few moves Black's pieces become ineffective for a defense against a triple attack on his weak KB2.

Black's avenues for King escapes are blocked by his own pieces. The unlucky Queen tries to ward off the fatal thrust by playing 26 ... Q–Q1, but this only quickens White's *coup de grâce*.

The opening is an old-fashioned one—but for how long? Many an ancient debut has been infused with new life by the recent research of Fischer, Benko, Bisguier, Keres, Euwe and the Soviet theorists. These renovators have also been true innovators, particularly in the Petroff Defense, the Center Counter, the Paulsen Line in the Sicilian Defense, the newly popular King's Indian and Queen's Indian defenses, and the King's Gambit.

Even the ancient Greco Counter Gambit has been revived with some Baltic frills and is now called the Latvian Gambit.

Position after 15 ... N/2-N3

NOTES TO THE GAME

a) Score yourself 3 points also if you selected 5 P-Q3 or 5 P-QN4.

b) Score yourself 2 points also for 7 N-B3 which produces the exciting Moeller Attack.

c) White trades space for the better Pawn position.

d) Here Kmoch recommends 10 ... O-O: e.g., 11 BxN, N-R4 12 BxP†, and Black gets play for the Pawn.

e) White threatens to win a piece.

f) On 17 ... K-B1, 18 NxP† wins.

---

†=check; ‡=double check; ⵜ=discovered check

ILL FARES THE GAME, TO HASTENING ILLS A PREY

Wheels of the Gods grind slowly, the saying goes, and it is so wth grandmasters, too. The line of the Lopez played here about 50 years ago crops up nowadays as something original and new. And the stock violent, King-side assault stings as much, too. Grandmaster Teichman (White) grants no draw to drawing master Schlechter after 1 P-K4, P-K4 2 N-KB3, N-QB3 3 B-N5, P-QR3 4 B-R4, N-B3 5 O-O.

Cover scoring table at line indicated. Set up position, make Black's next move (exposing table just enough to read it). Now guess White's 6th move, then expose it. Score par, if move agrees; zero, if not. Make move actually given, Black's reply. Then guess White's next, and so on.

COVER WHITE MOVES

IN TABLE BELOW.   **EXPOSE ONE LINE AT A TIME**

White Played	Par Score	Black Played	Your Selection for White's move	Your Score
		5 .... B-K2	-----------------	--------
6 R-K1	4	6 .... P-QN4	-----------------	--------
7 B-N3	3	7 .... P-Q3	-----------------	--------
8 P-B3	5	8 .... O-O	-----------------	--------
9 P-Q3 (a)	3	9 .... N-QR4	-----------------	--------
10 B-B2	4	10 .... P-B4	-----------------	--------
11 QN-Q2	4	11 .... Q-B2	-----------------	--------
12 N-B1	5	12 .... N-B3	-----------------	--------
13 N-K3	5	13 .... B-N2 (b)	-----------------	--------
14 N-B5	5	14 .... KR-K1	-----------------	--------
15 B-N5	5	15 .... N-Q2	-----------------	--------
16 B-N3	6	16 .... N-B1	-----------------	--------
17 B-Q5 (c)	6	17 .... N-N3	-----------------	--------
18 BxB	4	18 .... N/N3xB*	-----------------	--------
19 BxP†	8	19 .... KxB	-----------------	--------
20 N-N5†	5	20 .... K-N1 (d)	-----------------	--------
21 Q-R5	6	21 .... NxN	-----------------	--------
22 QxRP†	5	22 .... K-B1	-----------------	--------
23 QxN†	4	23 .... K-N1	-----------------	--------
24 Q-N6 (e)	7	24 .... Q-Q2	-----------------	--------
25 R-K3	6	25 .... Resigns	-----------------	--------
Total Score 100		Your Percentage -------------------		

SCALE: 75-100—Excellent; 55-74—Superior; 40-54—Good; 25-39—Fair

101

Notes on TEICHMAN vs. SCHLECHTER

Schlechter never made the same mistake twice. This was the first and last time he fianchettoed the Queen Bishop in the Black-side of a Ruy Lopez. Black's inaccuracy allows a White Knight to perch venomously on KB5. This is the underlying theme of White strategy in every Ruy.

Teichman exploits his advantage, and all the cajolings with Black's minor pieces cannot halt the disaster. Pertinent to White's attack is the ubiquitous King Bishop. Its every sortie is a threatening one, in marked contrast to the dead-end immobility of the Black Bishop on QN2.

Teichman was a tough competitor, and always achieved a high niche in every tournament he entered. Emanuel Lasker, Spielmann, Rubinstein, Tarrasch—all, at one time or another, also bowed to his adroit play.

In this game, Black never started a serious counter-attack. As Maroczy said: "Counter-attack is the soul of chess."

Position after 18 . . . N/N3xB

NOTES TO THE GAME

a) A slow line of the Ruy Lopez of half a century ago which is being revived today.

b) This Bishop is better posted on its original diagonal.

c) Now White threatens 18 BxN, followed by 19 NxB, and so forces Black's hand.

d) On either 20 . . . K-N3 or 20 . . . K-B3, White wins by 21 Q-N4.

e) Star move: there is no adequate defense against 25 R-K3-R3-R8†, with mate to follow.

† = check; ‡ = dbl. check; § = dis. check

SPECULATE TO ACCUMULATE

To produce wins, a player must saddle his opponent with problems, even at the expense of risk. What distinguishes the master from the expert is the appraisal of the risk. And Vienese Grandmaster Spielmann was a genius at drawing the fine line. Here he essays an inferior but befuddling Vienna and, in short order, his opponent Prokes, falls apart. The game begins with 1 P-K4, P-K4 2 N-QB3, N-KB3 3 P-B4, P-Q4, 4 PxKP.

Cover scoring table at line indicated. Set up position, make Black's next move (exposing table just enough to read it). Now guess White's 5th move, then expose it. Score par, if move agrees; zero, if not. Make move actually given, opponent's reply. Then guess White's next, and so on.

COVER WHITE MOVES
IN TABLE BELOW.   EXPOSE ONE LINE AT A TIME

White Played	Par Score	Black Played	Your Selection for White's move	Your Score
		4 .... NxP	------------------	--------
5 Q-B3 (a)	3	5 .... P-KB4	------------------	--------
6 P-Q3	5	6 .... NxN	------------------	--------
7 PxN	3	7 .... P-Q5	------------------	--------
8 Q-B2	7	8 .... PxP (b)	------------------	--------
9 P-Q4	5	9 .... B-K3 (c)	------------------	--------
10 N-R3	8	10 .... B-K2	------------------	--------
11 N-B4	7	11 .... Q-Q2	------------------	--------
12 NxB	6	12 .... QxN	------------------	--------
13 B-Q3	5	13 .... P-KN3	------------------	--------
14 Q-K2 (d)	5	14 .... Q-Q4*	------------------	--------
15 O-O	6	15 .... QxQP† (e)	------------------	--------
16 B-K3	6	16 .... Q-Q4	------------------	--------
17 QR-Q1	6	17 .... Q-R4	------------------	--------
18 BxBP (f)	8	18 .... R-B1	------------------	--------
19 Q-N4	8	19 .... PxB	------------------	--------
20 Q-R5†	6	20 .... R-B2	------------------	--------
21 P-K6	6	.... Resigns	------------------	--------
Total Score	100	Your Percentage ------------------		———

SCALE: 75-100—Excellent; 55-74—Superior; 40-54—Good; 25-39—Fair

Notes on SPIELMANN vs. PROKES

In character, Spielmann's play is sharp, provocative. His wide-open style edges Black (the Pawn-snatcher) into an indefensible King-side setup.

Prokes' maneuvers were a pretty good example of how not to play chess—*against Spielmann*, whose sacrificial combinations demanded open lines for Bishops and Rooks.

In the tourneys he entered, Spielmann, the author of *The Art of Sacrifice*, was an insistent worry to the highest-ranking opponents. One could never be sure when one of Spielmann's inspirations would upset the chess

*Position after 14 . . . Q–Q4

Notes to the Game

(a) A tricky move which leads to nought after 5 . . . N-QB3. Take equal credit for 5 N-B3 or 5 P-Q3.

(b) Better is 8 . . . N-B3.

(c) Black ought to crack the center with 9 . . . P-B4.

(d) White prepares for B-QB4.

(e) Black is neglecting his development. 15 . . . N-B3, followed by Queen-side castling, is best.

(f) The violent breakthrough. There is no longer any defense.

---

†=check; ‡=double check; §=discovered check

WAR OF NERVES

TALENT AND COURAGE versus talent and courage produces boundless excitement — the epic battle. Here, at Berlin, 1920, Grandmaster Tarrasch (White) engages Grandmaster Tartakover in an unorthodox Queen Pawn Opening, a variation of the Albin Counter Gambit. The debut is dangerous for both sides. The game begins with 1 P–Q4, P–Q4 2 P–QB4, P–K4 3 PxKP, P–Q5 4 N–KB3, P–QB4 5 P–K3, N–QB3 6 PxP.

Cover scoring table at line indicated. Set up position, make Black's next move (exposing table just enough to read it). Now guess White's 7th move, then expose it. Score par if your move agrees; zero, if not. Make move actually given, opponent's reply. Then guess White's next and so on.

COVER WHITE MOVES
IN TABLE BELOW.   EXPOSE ONE LINE AT A TIME

White Played	Par Score	Black Played	Your Selection for White's move	Your Score
		6 .... PxP	----------------	--------
7 B–Q3 ------ 3		7 .... KN–K2 (a)	----------------	--------
8 QN–Q2 ---- 3		8 .... B–KN5	----------------	--------
9 Q–N3 ------ 3		9 .... Q–B2	----------------	--------
10 O–O ------- 3		10 .... O–O–O	----------------	--------
11 R–K1 ------ 3		11 .... N–N3	----------------	--------
12 P–KR3 ---- 3		12 .... B–K3!	----------------	--------
13 B–K4! ----- 4		13 .... N/NxP	----------------	--------
14 NxN ------- 3		14 .... QxN	----------------	--------
15 N–B3 ------ 3		15 .... Q–QB4	----------------	--------
16 B–B4 (b) * 6		16 .... B–Q3	----------------	--------
17 BxN ------- 5		17 .... PxB	----------------	--------
18 BxB ------- 3		18 .... RxB (c)	----------------	--------
19 N–K5 ------ 3		19 .... KR–Q1	----------------	--------
20 Q–R4 (d) -- 4		20 .... P–Q6	----------------	--------
21 P–QN4 ----- 3		21 .... Q–Q5	----------------	--------
22 NxQBP ---- 4		22 .... RxN	----------------	--------
23 QxR† ------ 3		23 .... K–N1	----------------	--------
24 P–B5 ------ 3		24 .... P–Q7	----------------	--------
25 KR–Q1 ---- 3		25 .... B–B4	----------------	--------
26 Q–N5† ----- 3		26 .... K–B2	----------------	--------
27 Q–R5† ----- 3		27 .... K–N1	----------------	--------
28 P–N5 ------ 4		28 .... B–B7	----------------	--------
29 P–N6 ------ 4		29 .... R–Q2	----------------	--------
30 PxP† ------ 4		30 .... K–R1	----------------	--------
31 P–B6 ------ 4		31 .... R–Q4	----------------	--------
32 P–B7 ------ 4		32 .... B–B4	----------------	--------
33 P–B8(Q)† -- 5		33 .... BxQ	----------------	--------
34 Q–B7 (e) -- 4		34 .... Resigns	----------------	--------

Total Score   100 | Your Percentage --------------------

SCALE: 75-100—Excellent: 55-74—Superior: 40-54—Good: 25-39—Fair

Notes on TARRASCH vs. TARTAKOVER

Tartakover was only happy resurrecting some long-forgotten or long-abandoned opening. Gilding it with his own refinements, he would release the re-awakened mummy during important tournaments.

In the great New York Tournament of 1924, Tartakover twice, with the White pieces, played 1 P–K4, P–K4 2 P–KB4, PxP 3 B–K2, a debut known as the Lesser Bishop's Gambit. This is supposed to be better for White than 3 B–B4 because Black has not the immediate effective counter 3 . . . P–Q4. The opening with 3 B–K2 could very well be dubbed "Tartakover's own." Strangely enough, experiment as he did with strange themes in the openings, no debut has been named after him. (*En passant*, Tartakover scored two draws with the above eccentricity in New York, 1924.)

The opening here is equated by Dr. Emanuel Lasker as offering practical chances for Black. There is one amusing variation which entails a neat trap, whereby Black effects three Knights, with an easy win:

1 P–Q4, P–Q4 2 P–QB4, P–K4 3 PxKP, P–Q5 4 P–K3? B–N5 ch 5 B–Q2, PxP 6 BxB, PxP ch 7 K–K2, PxN promoting to a Knight with check and wins. (7 ... PxN(Q) does not work because of 8 QxQ ch, etc. Neither does 7 ... B–N5 ch? because of 8 N–B3!)

*Position after 16 B-B4

NOTES TO THE GAME

a) Not 7 . . . NxP 8 Q-K2 (if 8 NxN? Q-R4†) as White wins a Pawn.

b) A profound combination. On 16 . . . BxP 17 QxB, QxQ 18 B-B5†, R-Q2 19 R-K8†, N-Q1 20 N-K5, White wins.

c) At first sight, all seems well for Black. All is not what it seems.

d) With these last two moves, White has secured the win of material, as appears on the next move.

e) This game won the brilliancy prize.

†=check; ‡=double check; §=discovered check

TRIPLE IMMUNITY

In the top echelon, opening play requires precision, finesse and subtlety. At Leningrad, 1936, Konstantinopolsky (White) leaves his King Pawn unprotected three times. Panov quite correctly refrains from capturing. And the indomitable King Pawn helps clinch the win. The opening, an Old Indian, begins: 1 P–Q4, N–KB3 2 P–QB4, P–Q3 3 N–QB3, QN–Q2 4 P–K4, P–K4 5 KN–K2, B–K2 6 P–KN3.

Cover scoring table at line indicated. Set up position, make Black's next move (exposing table just enough to read it). Now guess White's 7th move, then expose it. Score par, if move agrees; zero, if not. Make move actually given, Black's reply. Then guess White's next, and so on.

COVER WHITE MOVES
IN TABLE BELOW.   **EXPOSE ONE LINE AT A TIME**

White Played	Par Score	Black Played	Your Selection for White's move	Your Score
		6 .... O–O	....	....
7 B–N2	2	7 .... R–K1	....	....
8 O–O	2	8 .... B–B1	....	....
9 P–N3	3	9 .... P–B3	....	....
10 B–N2	2	10 .... Q–B2	....	....
11 P–KR3	3	11 .... P–QR3	....	....
12 P–QR4	4	12 .... P–QN3	....	....
13 P–B4	4	13 .... B–N2	....	....
14 R–B1	3	14 .... PxQP	....	....
15 NxP	3	15 .... P–B4	....	....
16 N–B5	5	16 .... P–N3 (a)	....	....
17 N–K3	3	17 .... B–N2 (b)	....	....
18 Q–B2	2	18 .... R–K2	....	....
19 P–KN4	5	19 .... R/2–K1 (c)	....	....
20 P–N5	3	20 .... N–R4	....	....
21 N/B–Q5	...4	21 .... Q–Q1	....	....
22 BxB	3	22 .... NxB	....	....
23 N–N4	4	23 .... BxN	....	....
24 BPxB	4	24 .... R–R2	....	....
25 R/QB–K1	..4	25 .... R–B1	....	....
26 N–R6†	4	26 .... K–R1	....	....
27 P–K5!	5	27 .... PxP	....	....
28 PxP	3	28 .... Q–K2	....	....
29 Q–B3	4	29 .... P–N4	....	....
30 P–K6	5	30 .... BPxP	....	....
31 QPxP	3	31 .... RxR†	....	....
32 RxR	3	32 .... P–N5*	....	....
33 Q–R1	4	33 .... QxKP	....	....
34 R–K1!	4	34 .... Q–Q3	....	....
35 N–B7†	2	Resigns	....	....

| Total Score . 100 | Your Percentage .... | |

SCALE: 75-100—Excellent; 55-74—Superior; 40-54—Good; 25-39—Fair

Notes on KONSTANTINOPOLSKY vs. PANOV

This game is an instructive illustration of how properly timed moves can stitch a straitjacket around a conventional defense. Not once during the game has White a material advantage; the lumber on each side is approximately equal. But from the first few moves White controls more space.

Black is guilty of handling his Rooks in a wavering manner, and his castled King's position becomes too loose against an enemy Pawn at White's KN5.

White's monarch is securely nestled behind his fianchettoed Bishop, with the gallant Knight's Pawn ready to advance in kamikaze style against the Black King. To ward off this threat by a foot soldier, a Black Knight finds himself in a doubly awkward spot. The horseman is immobile because of a "pin" by the adverse Queen and at the same time he blocks off the last exit for his own ruler.

If the later Black moves were forced, then his opening scheme was badly conceived, though in the debut there is no particular move which bears the onus.

*Position after 32 ... P–N5

NOTES TO THE GAME

a) The first instance of immunity: on 16 ... NxP 17 NxN, BxB 18 BxB, RxB 19 N–R6†, K–R1 20 NxP†, K–N1 21 Q–Q5, White threatens two Rooks and mate.

b) Second instance: here, if 17 ... NxP 18 N/K–Q5, BxN 19 NxB, Q–N2 20 Q–Q3, P–B4, White has 21 N–B7, winning the Exchange for 21 ... QxN loses to 22 Q–Q5†.

c) Third instance: now Black can try 19... QR–K1 20 P–N5, NxP but then runs into 21 N/B–Q5, BxN 22 NxB, losing the Exchange.

† = check; ‡ = double check; § = dis. check

108

ST. GEORGE AND MERRIE ENGLAND

THE DRAGON VARIATION is sure death to the timid. To the courageous, it is a welcome challenge. Here English amateur, F. W. Allen
(White) extracts its fangs and clobbers the poor dragon (H. Brown) in
the Surrey Championship of 1954. The game begins with 1 P-K4, P-QB4
2 N-KB3, N-QB3 3 P-Q4, PxP 4 NxP, N-B3 5 N-QB3.

Cover the scoring table at line indicated. Set up position, make
Black's 5th move (exposing table just enough to read it). Guess White's
move, then expose next line. Score par if your move agrees; if not, zero.
Make move given, opponent's reply. Guess White's next, and so on to
the end.

COVER WHITE MOVES

IN TABLE BELOW.   EXPOSE ONE LINE AT A TIME

White Played	Par Score	Black Played	Your Selection for White's move	Your Score
		5 .... P-Q3	----------------	---------
6 P-B3 (a)	5	6 .... P-KN3	----------------	---------
7 B-K3	3	7 .... B-N2	----------------	---------
8 Q-Q2	2	8 .... O-O	----------------	---------
9 O-O-O	3	9 .... N-Q2 (b)	----------------	---------
10 P-KN4	4	10 .... N/2-K4	----------------	---------
11 B-K2	2	11 .... N-R4	----------------	---------
12 P-N3	3	12 .... QN-B3 (c)	----------------	---------
13 P-KR4	5	13 .... Q-R4	----------------	---------
14 P-R5	4	14 .... B-Q2	----------------	---------
15 PxP	2	15 .... BPxP (d)	----------------	---------
16 P-B4!	5	16 .... NxP	----------------	---------
17 B-B4†	5	17 .... K-R1*	----------------	---------
18 RxP†!! (e)	8	18 .... KxR	----------------	---------
19 R-R1†	7	19 .... N-R3	----------------	---------
20 P-B5	6	20 .... P-KN4	----------------	---------
21 BxP	3	21 .... R-B3	----------------	---------
22 BxR	3	22 .... PxB	----------------	---------
23 NxN	3	23 .... PxN	----------------	---------
24 Q-N2! (f)	5	24 .... P-Q4	----------------	---------
25 Q-N6†	3	25 .... K-R1	----------------	---------
26 RxN†	4	26 .... BxR	----------------	---------
27 QxB†	3	27 .... K-N1	----------------	---------
28 NxP	6	28 .... PxN	----------------	---------
29 BxP†	4	29 .... QxB	----------------	---------
30 PxQ	2	.... Resigns	----------------	---------
Total Score	100	Your Percentage	----------------	---------

SCALE: 75-100—Excellent; 55-74—Superior; 40-54—Good; 25-39—Fair

Notes on ALLEN vs. BROWN

This sort of attack (with variations), known these days as the Porcupine Attack, was thought, a few years ago, to have demolished the Dragon Variation of the Sicilian Defense. Nevertheless, Sammy Reshevsky, the veteran American grandmaster, has persisted in adopting the Dragon in important tourneys and matches. Even though the Dragon's death knell had been sounded(?) Reshevsky has produced a plus score with this debut.

Most other grandmasters, however, prefer in the Sicilian to develop the King's Bishop toward the center, combining this with the hyper-

Position after 17 . . . K-R1

NOTES TO THE GAME

(a) With castles long, known 20 years ago as the Intercollegiate Attack, this system is now in vogue with the masters.

(b) The question mark move, seemingly sound but unsuccessful in practical play. 9 . . . NxN 10 BxN, Q-R4 11 K-N1, P-K4, followed by 12 . . . B-K3 is the book continuation.

(c) This "provoke and retreat" strategy fails here. Even so, 12 . . . B-Q2 13 P-KR4 gives White a strong initiative.

(d) 15 . . . RPxP, and a prayer!

(e) A stock sacrifice, dangerous for both.

(f) Now there's no defense. A great game.

110

GEOMETRIC ILLUSION

THERE is a geometric proposition that the whole is equal to the sum of its parts. This may be true, generally. But not with Keres. He apparently sacs more pieces than are on the board and still has enough to administer mate. Here Eliskases (Black) is on the receiving end at Semmering, 1937, in a Wing Gambit Deferred. The game begins with 1 P-K4, P-QB4 2 N-KB3, P-Q3 3 P-QN4, PxP 4 P-Q4, N-KB3 5 B-Q3.

Cover scoring table at line indicated. Set up position, make Black's 5th move (exposing table just enough to read that move). Guess White's move, expose next line. Score par if your move agrees; if not, zero. Make move given, opponent's reply. Guess White's next, and so on to end.

COVER WHITE MOVES

IN TABLE BELOW.   **EXPOSE ONE LINE AT A TIME**

White Played	Par Score	Black Played	Your Selection for White's move	Your Score
		5 .... P-Q4	-----------------	--------
6 QN-Q2	2	6 .... PxP	-----------------	--------
7 NxP	2	7 .... QN-Q2	-----------------	--------
8 QN-N5	4	8 .... Q-B2 (a)	-----------------	--------
9 P-B4	4	9 .... P-KR3 (b)	-----------------	--------
10 N-R3	1	10 .... P-KN4	-----------------	--------
11 N/R3-N1	1	11 .... B-N2	-----------------	--------
12 N-K2	2	12 .... P-K4	-----------------	--------
13 N-N3	3	13 .... O-O	-----------------	--------
14 O-O	3	14 .... P-K5	-----------------	--------
15 NxKP	3	15 .... NxN	-----------------	--------
16 BxN	2	16 .... QxP	-----------------	--------
17 B-Q3	3	17 .... Q-Q4	-----------------	--------
18 R-K1	5	18 .... P-N5	-----------------	--------
19 N-R4	4	19 .... N-N3 (c)	-----------------	--------
20 R-N1	4	20 .... B-Q2	-----------------	--------
21 R-K4	4	21 .... KR-K1	-----------------	--------
22 R-B4	4	22 .... Q-Q3	-----------------	--------
23 B-Q2	3	23 .... N-Q4 *	-----------------	--------
24 RxKNP	7	24 .... BxR (d)	-----------------	--------
25 QxB	3	25 .... Q-KB3	-----------------	--------
26 N-B5	4	26 .... K-B1	-----------------	--------
27 NxB	4	27 .... QxN	-----------------	--------
28 Q-R5	4	28 .... N-B3	-----------------	--------
29 Q-R4	4	29 .... P-KR4	-----------------	--------
30 RxP	7	30 .... QR-B1	-----------------	--------
31 P-KR3	3	31 .... R-B2	-----------------	--------
32 R-N5	5	32 .... R-K3	-----------------	--------
33 RxRP	5	33 .... Resigns (e)	-----------------	--------
Total Score	100	Your Percentage ----------------		--------

SCALE: 75-100—Excellent; 55-74—Superior; 40-54—Good; 25-39—Fair

Notes on KERES vs. ELISKASES

This game is typical of Keres' elegant and richly subtle play. It is noteworthy that the sacrifice of the Exchange is an abiding theme in the victories of attacking players. The motif is this: Two side-by-side Bishops slanting against the enemy King activate more powerfully than the cumbersome Rooks of the opposition.

Keres possesses a remarkable genius for combinations of the most far-reaching order; only Alekhine equaled him in this respect. Keres has great theoretical knowledge and sound positional understanding. In inferior positions he is cool and resourceful.

It is pertinent to note that the key move of White's gambit, P–QN4, is better deferred until Black has played . . . P–Q3.

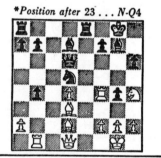

*Position after 23 . . . N-Q4

† = check; ‡ = dbl. check; § = dis. ch.

NOTES TO THE GAME

a) 8 . . . P-KR3 9 N-K6! followed by 10 NxB, leaves Black with a disrupted development. Of course not 9 . . . PxN 10 B-N6 mate.

b) If 9 . . . PxP e.p. 10 Q-N3, P-K3 11 NxP, Black's defenses are shattered.

c) 19 . . . QxQP looks dangerous but is really correct: 20 N-B5? QxR 21 QxP, K-R1, and White has only skin and bones.

d) Poor judgment. 24 . . . N-B6 is double-edged. The text is all for White.

e) There is no defense to 34 R-N5 or 34 B-R6 or 33 . . . NxR 34 Q-Q8† and 35 B-N4†.

A WORD TO THE HYPERMODERN-WISE

THIS GAME is an anachronism. It begins on a hypermodern note despite its dateline of 1912. Yet it echoes the classical brilliancy of the Eighteen Hundreds. The slow, plodding positional game that Black (Loewenfisch) had planned is rent asunder by a few deft strokes. For White is Alekhine. The game, at the St. Petersburg C. C. Tournament begins with 1 P-Q4.

Cover scoring table at line indicated. Set up position, make Black's 1st move (exposing table just enough to read it). Now guess White's next, expose next line. Score par if your move agrees; if not, score zero. Make move given and opponent's reply. Then guess White's next, and so on to end.

**COVER WHITE MOVES
IN TABLE BELOW.**
                              EXPOSE ONE LINE AT A TIME

White Played	Par Score	Black Played	Your Selection for White's move	Your Score
		1 .... P-QB4 (a)	----------------	--------
2 P-Q5	4	2 .... N-KB3	----------------	--------
3 N-QB3	4	3 .... P-Q3	----------------	--------
4 P-K4	4	4 .... P-KN3	----------------	--------
5 P-B4	6	5 .... QN-Q2	----------------	--------
6 N-B3	4	6 .... P-QR3	----------------	--------
7 P-K5 (b)	7	7 .... PxP	----------------	--------
8 PxP	3	8 .... N-N5	----------------	--------
9 P-K6	7	9 .... QN-K4	----------------	--------
10 B-KB4	5	10 .... NxN†	----------------	--------
11 PxN	6	11 .... N-B3	----------------	--------
12 B-B4	5	12 .... PxP (c)	----------------	--------
13 PxP	3	13 .... Q-N3 (d)	----------------	--------
14 Q-K2	8	14 .... QxNP *	----------------	--------
15 N-N5	9	15 .... QxR†	----------------	--------
16 K-B2 (e)	10	16 .... QxR	----------------	--------
17 N-B7†	6	17 .... K-Q1	----------------	--------
18 Q-Q2†	5	18 .... B-Q2	----------------	--------
19 PxB	4	19 .... Resigns	----------------	--------
Total Score	100	Your Percentage	----------------------	------

SCALE: 75-100—Excellent; 55-74—Superior; 40-54—Good; 25-39—Fair

Notes on ALEKHINE vs. LOEWENFISCH

Znosko-Borovsky, a countryman of Loewenfisch, wrote a best seller: *How Not to Play Chess*. Black's game is a good example. After muddling his development, leaving his King unprotected, Loewenfisch has nothing more to lose by sending his Queen on a Pawn-and-Rook-grabbing voyage.

Black's Pawn skeleton is as full of holes as a sieve, and after 15 N–N5 there is no possible defense.

Black's opening move 1 . . . P–QB4 is not bad per se. This is the current Benoni Defense, which is a tenacious debut for Black if it is conducted cautiously move by move. Here, Black's 2 . . . N–KB3 is very premature, as it sets up quickly the target for White's sharp drive against the Black bastion.

Position after 14 . . . QxNP

Notes to the Game

a) The hypermodern idea—played in 1912! Black provokes the advance of White's center Pawns, hoping they will prove weak.

b) White not only provokes "easy," he throws caution and Pawns to the winds.

c) Relatively better is 12 . . . B-N2.

d) Exchanging Queens does not ease the bind. Threats of B-B7 and N-N5, among others, are implicit in the position.

e) The double Rook sacrifice is an echo of the immortal Anderssen-Kieseritzky game.

THERE IS NOTHING NEW UNDER THE SUN

Heyday for American champion Frank J. Marshall was his victory at Cambridge Springs, 1904. Not only did he tower over the mightiest from the rest of the world but also he vanquished his renowned countryman, Harry Nelson Pillsbury, in magnificent style. And he (White) did so in what is now considered a (Black) hypermodern defense. This King's Indian begins with 1 P–Q4, P–Q3 2 P–K4, N–KB3 3 N–QB3.

Cover scoring table at line indicated. Set up position, make Black's next move (exposing table just enough to read it). Now guess White's 4th move, then expose it. Score par, if move agrees; zero, if not. Make move actually given, opponent's reply. Then guess White's next, and so on.

COVER WHITE MOVES

IN TABLE BELOW.   EXPOSE ONE LINE AT A TIME

White Played	Par Score	Black Played	Your Selection for White's move	Your Score
		3 . . . . P–KN3	-----------------	--------
4 P–B4	4	4 . . . . B–N2 (a)	-----------------	--------
5 P–K5 (b)	5	5 . . . . PxP (c)	-----------------	--------
6 BPxP	5	6 . . . . N–Q4	-----------------	--------
7 N–B3	3	7 . . . . N–QB3	-----------------	--------
8 B–QB4	5	8 . . . . P–K3 (d)	-----------------	--------
9 B–KN5	5	9 . . . . NxN	-----------------	--------
10 PxN	3	10 . . . . N–K2	-----------------	--------
11 O–O	3	11 . . . . P–KR3	-----------------	--------
12 B–B6 (e)	9	12 . . . . BxB	-----------------	--------
13 PxB	3	13 . . . . N–B4	-----------------	--------
14 Q–K2	5	14 . . . . QxBP (f)	-----------------	--------
15 P–N4	5	15 . . . . N–Q3	-----------------	--------
16 N–K5	5	16 . . . . Q–K2	-----------------	--------
17 B–Q3	6	17 . . . . O–O	-----------------	--------
18 R–B2	5	18 . . . . K–N2	-----------------	--------
19 QR–KB1	5	19 . . . . B–Q2	-----------------	--------
20 R–B6 (g)	8	20 . . . . R–KN1*	-----------------	--------
21 NxNP	7	21 . . . . QxR (h)	-----------------	--------
22 RxQ	3	22 . . . . KxR	-----------------	--------
23 Q–K5 mate	6			

Total Score   100   Your Percentage ---------------------

SCALE: 75-100—Excellent; 55-74—Superior; 40-54—Good; 25-39—Fair

Notes on MARSHALL vs. PILLSBURY

Marshall was in his prime when this game was played. Pillsbury was a sick man, with only two more years to live.

Black is not to be condemned for adopting a debut which at that time was considered eccentric. Up to 4 . . . B–N2, all is correct according to current treatment; but then Black played carelessly by opening up the game with a Pawn exchange. This debut demands the modern "waiting" style.

Pillsbury, however, relies on open-board tactics. (which had brought him many victories) to combat similar tactics on Marshall's part. This is a strategical mistake here.

Marshall's attack is a model one, in which *tempo* and space-control clinch the win.

*Position after 20 . . . R–KN1

NOTES TO THE GAME

a) A contemporary defense, played some fifty odd years ago!

b) White seeks immediate refutation.

c) Here 5 . . . KN-Q2 is safer.

d) And now 8 . . . N-N3 is better. The text creates holes.

e) A profound Pawn sacrifice.

f) Risky; but necessary, sooner or later.

g) A la Marshall.

h) Of course, 21 . . . PxN 22 RxP† is also fatal for Black.

---

†=check; ‡=double check; ‡=discovered check

ON THE ROAD TO WORLD SUPREMACY

What are the ingredients of a champion, that is the question. Talent, of course, and tenacity, the killer instinct and the desire to see one's opponent squirm, these seem to be the answer. Here, in 1947 at Moscow, Grandmaster Smyslov (White) makes his opponent Plater look like a "selling plater." The opening of the game is a King's Indian Defense which begins with the moves: 1 P-QB4, N-KB3 2 N-KB3, P-KN3 3 P-KN3, B-N2 4 B-N2, O-O 5 O-O. (Before looking below, read following instructions.)

Cover scoring table at line indicated. Set up position, make Black's next move (exposing table just enough to read it). Now guess White's 6th move, then expose it. Score par, if move agrees; zero, if not. Make move actually given, Black's reply. Then guess White's next, and so on.

COVER WHITE MOVES
IN TABLE BELOW.   EXPOSE ONE LINE AT A TIME

White Played	Par Score	Black Played	Your Selection for White's move	Your Score
		5 . . . . P-Q3	----------------	--------
6 P-Q4	4	6 . . . . QN-Q2	----------------	--------
7 N-B3	4	7 . . . . P-K4	----------------	--------
8 P-K4	6	8 . . . . P-B3	----------------	--------
9 R-K1	4	9 . . . . Q-B2	----------------	--------
10 P-KR3	6	10 . . . . PxP (a)	----------------	--------
11 NxP	4	11 . . . . N-N3	----------------	--------
12 P-N3	4	12 . . . . R-K1	----------------	--------
13 B-N5	6	13 . . . . P-QR4	----------------	--------
14 Q-Q2	5	14 . . . . P-R5	----------------	--------
15 QR-Q1	5	15 . . . . PxP	----------------	--------
16 PxP	4	16 . . . . QN-Q2	----------------	--------
17 B-R6	7	17 . . . . B-R1 (b)	----------------	--------
18 N-B5 (c)	9	18 . . . . N-B4	----------------	--------
19 NxP	4	19 . . . . R-K2	----------------	--------
20 P-QN4	4	20 . . . . N-K3	----------------	--------
21 P-B5	5	21 . . . . P-N3	----------------	--------
22 P-K5	6	22 . . . . N-Q2?*	----------------	--------
23 BxP (d)	3	23 . . . . Resigns (e)	----------------	--------
Total Score 100		Your Percentage ----------------		--------

SCALE: 75-100—Excellent; 55-74—Superior; 40-54—Good; 25-39—Fair

Notes on SMYSLOV vs. PLATER

The denouement here can be likened to an earthquake in the middle of a flowery plain at the sunset hour of a sunny afternoon.

A brilliancy, but how strangely different from the brilliancies of the romantic school! Here are no preliminary harrowings, sharp sorties, ambushes, assaults, peppery counter-attacks, slashing defenses.

Everything has proceeded (seemingly) most decorously on both sides. White, of course, has (seemingly) only a slight positional pull. Then White's Bishop captures the Black Pawn. Black's rafters crash and engulf him.

A modern-style game par excellence, with a bizarre finale. Like the sight of a redheaded woman on a white horse in the middle of Main Street.

Position after 23 BxP

Notes to the Game

Score yourself 4 points also on other reasonable developing moves on moves 6, 7 and 9.

a) Here Black cedes the center; but it is difficult for him to develop a constructive plan.

b) A critical blunder. 17 . . . N-B4 is the move, tempting the advance of the Queenside Pawns with a view to weakening them.

c) White wins a vital Pawn by force.

d) A star move which crushes all resistance.

e) On 23 . . . QxB, White has 24 N-Q5, and Black is helpless.

---

†=check; ‡=double check; ⸸=discovered check

DE GUSTIBUS NON DISPUTANDUM

Master of attack and author of the *Art of Sacrifice in Chess*, Rudolf Spielmann (White) confirms his claim to fame in this adventurous debut versus Honlinger in one of their early match games in 1925. From the seventeenth move on, every move makes the rafters ring, culminating in a grand finale. The opening, a Caro-Kann begins with 1 P-K4, P-QB3 2 P-Q4, P-Q4 3 N-QB3, PxP 4 NxP, N-B3 5 N-N3.

Cover scoring table at line indicated. Set up position, make Black's next move (exposing table just enough to read it). Now guess White's 6th move, then expose it. Score par, if move agrees; zero, if not. Make move actually given, opponent's reply. Then guess White's next, and so on.

COVER WHITE MOVES

IN TABLE BELOW.   **EXPOSE ONE LINE AT A TIME**

White Played	Par Score	Black Played	Your Selection for White's move	Your Score
		5 . . . P-K3 (a)	-------------------	--------
6 N-B3	3	6 . . . . P-B4	-------------------	--------
7 B-Q3	5	7 . . . . N-B3	-------------------	--------
8 PxP	4	8 . . . . BxP	-------------------	--------
9 P-QR3	5	9 . . . . O-O	-------------------	--------
10 O-O	3	10 . . . . P-QN3	-------------------	--------
11 P-N4	5	11 . . . . B-K2	-------------------	--------
12 B-N2	3	12 . . . . Q-B2	-------------------	--------
13 P-N5	5	13 . . . . N-QR4	-------------------	--------
14 N-K5	4	14 . . . . B-N2	-------------------	--------
15 N-N4	6	15 . . . . Q-Q1 (b)	-------------------	--------
16 N-K3	3	16 . . . . N-Q4	-------------------	--------
17 Q-R5	6	17 . . . . P-N3	-------------------	--------
18 N-N4	6	18 . . . B-KB3	-------------------	--------
19 NxB†	5	19 . . . . NxN	-------------------	--------
20 Q-R6	5	20 . . . . R-B1	-------------------	--------
21 QR-Q1	5	21 . . . . Q-K2	-------------------	--------
22 KR-K1	5	22 . . . . N-K1	-------------------	--------
23 N-B5	6	23 . . . . Q-B4 (c)	-------------------	--------
24 R-K5	6	24 . . . B-Q4 *	-------------------	--------
Mate in 4 (d)	10			

Total Score 100		Your Percentage ----------------		------

SCALE: 75-100—Excellent; 55-74—Superior; 40-54—Good; 25-39—Fair

Notes on SPIELMANN vs. HONLINGER

White's underlying theme, with a two-Bishop setup raking against the enemy King, is to force the weakening move 17 . . . P–KN3. After creating this gaping breach in the King's sanctuary, a White victory is a matter of correct timing. Every Black move now to the end is forced.

Black is to be censured not for his middle-game deployment which was stringently limited, but for his inconsistency in the opening. The admirable idea in the Caro-Kann is to challenge White's center Pawn without closing in the Black Queen's Bishop. But on move 5 . . . P–K3, Black is guilty of an unpardonable inconsistency and is bound to suffer the consequence.

* Position after 24 . . . B–Q4

Notes to the Game

a) Somewhat better is 5 . . . P-K4; on 6 PxP, QxQ† 7 KxQ, Black recovers his Pawn with 7 . . . N-N5.

b) To prevent 16 NxN†, BxN 17 BxB, PxB 18 Q-R5, P-B4 19 Q-N5†, K-R1 20 Q-B6†, K-N1 21 N-R5, etc.

c) Or 23 . . . NPxN 24 BxP! P-B3 25 BxKP†, followed by 26 BxR.

d) Score the 10 if you foresaw 25 N-K7†! for the sequel: 25 . . . QxN 26 QxRP†!! KxQ 27 R-R5†, K-N1 28 R-R8 mate.

†=check; ‡=double check; ‡=discovered check

The Simple Move is the Best Move. Find it!

WHAT is so rare as a game in which both players reach for the initiative? At Leningrad, 1935, Hungarian master Lilienthal essays the double-edged Budapest but is repulsed by Soviet's Alatortzeff who seizes the lead and by positional incursions mounts the pressure until Black's game gives. The opening: 1 P–Q4, N–KB3 2 P–QB4, P–K4 3 PxP, N–N5 4 P–K4.

Cover scoring table at line indicated. Set up position, make Black's next move (exposing table just enough to read it). Now guess White's 5th move, then expose it. Score par if your move agrees; zero, if not. Make move actually given, opponent's reply. Then guess White's next, and so on.

COVER WHITE MOVES

IN TABLE BELOW.   **EXPOSE ONE LINE AT A TIME**

White Played	Par Score	Black Played	Your Selection for White's move	Your Score
		4 .... NxP	------------------	--------
5 P–B4	4	5 .... KN–B3	------------------	--------
6 B–K3	3	6 .... B–N5†	------------------	--------
7 N–B3	3	7 .... Q–K2	------------------	--------
8 B–Q3	3	8 .... N–R3 (a)	------------------	--------
9 N–K2	4	9 .... O–O	------------------	--------
10 O–O	3	10 .... B–B4	------------------	--------
11 B–KB2	4	11 .... P–Q3	------------------	--------
12 N–Q5	4	12 .... Q–Q1 (b)	------------------	--------
13 P–QR3	3	13 .... BxB†	------------------	--------
14 RxB	3	14 .... N–B4	------------------	--------
15 B–B2	3	15 .... P–B4 (c)	------------------	--------
16 N–N3	4	16 .... NxP	------------------	--------
17 NxN	3	17 .... PxN	------------------	--------
18 BxP	3	18 .... B–B4	------------------	--------
19 BxB	3	19 .... RxB	------------------	--------
20 Q–N4	4	20 .... R–B2	------------------	--------
21 R–K1	4	21 .... N–K2	------------------	--------
22 N–B3	4	22 .... N–N3?	------------------	--------
23 P–KN3	3	23 .... Q–QB1	------------------	--------
24 Q–B3	3	24 .... R–N1	------------------	--------
25 R/2–K2	4	25 .... R–B1	------------------	--------
26 Q–Q5†	5	26 .... K–R1	------------------	--------
27 R–K6	4	27 .... R–Q1	------------------	--------
28 N–K4	4	28 .... N–B1	------------------	--------
29 R–K7	3	29 .... N–N3	------------------	--------
30 N–N5! (d)*	5	30 .... P–KR3	------------------	--------
31 RxP	7	31 .... Resigns	------------------	--------

Total Score 100 | **Your Percentage** ---------------------

SCALE: 75-100—Excellent; 55-74—Superior; 40-54—Good; 25-39—Fair

Notes on ALATORTZEFF vs. LILIENTHAL

About two decades ago, this opening (the Budapest Defense) was quite stylish—a fad with the avant-garde. Its popularity did not last. Black's development as played here (all in all) is too spotty and seems without force.

No doubt, the inadequacy of this defense stems primarily from having to play the King's Knight twice during the first three moves—truly a sortie that violates a rule of classic chess theory.

Black's early and violent attempt to disturb the normal Pawn formation may possibly pay off against a player meeting the Budapest for the first time. For instance:

1 P–Q4, N–KB3 2 P–QB4, P–K4 3 PxP, N–N5 4 P–B4? B–B4—and Black has the better game.

Position after 30 N-N5!

NOTES TO THE GAME

a) Inconsistent. 8 . . . BxN† at least shatters the adverse Pawn position. From here in, White controls the important center and remains with the superior development.

b) Abject retreat, tied to Black's 8th.

c) Premature. Black ought not to open lines while lagging in development; the lines will fall to White.

d) There is no defense: e.g., 31 . . . NxR yields Philidor's Legacy: 32 N-B7†, K-N1 33 N-R6‡, K-R1 34 Q-N8†, etc.

---

†=check; ‡=double check; §=discovered check

122

PEPPERY ASSAULT

Tall maneuvering to win an outpost precedes a sharp and daring assault in this game between Blackburne (White) and John at Ostend, 1906. The opening, a Four Knights, begins with 1 P–K4, P–K4 2 N–QB3, N–QB3 3 N–B3, N–B3 4 B–K2, B–N5 5 N–Q5.

Cover scoring table at line indicated. Set up position, make Black's next move (exposing table just enough to read it). Now guess White's 6th move, then expose it. Score par, if move agrees: zero, if not. Make move actually given, Black's reply. Then guess White's next, and so on.

COVER WHITE MOVES IN TABLE BELOW.　　**EXPOSE ONE LINE AT A TIME**

White Played	Par Score	Black Played	Your Selection for White's move	Your Score
		5 .... B–Q3 (a)	....	....
6 NxN†	 1	6 .... QxN	....	....
7 O–O	 3	7 .... P–KR3	....	....
8 P–B3	 3	8 .... B–K2	....	....
9 P–Q4	 3	9 .... P–Q3	....	....
10 P–Q5	 3	10 .... N–N1	....	....
11 N–K1	 4	11 .... P–KN4	....	....
12 N–B2	 3	12 .... N–Q2	....	....
13 N–K3	 3	13 .... N–B1	....	....
14 Q–R4†	... 5	14 .... K–Q1 (b)	....	....
15 B–N4 (c)	. 4	15 .... N–N3	....	....
16 BxB	 3	16 .... KxB	....	....
17 N–B5	 4	17 .... P–KR4	....	....
18 B–K3	 3	18 .... N–B5	....	....
19 P–B4	 3	19 .... K–N1 (d)	....	....
20 Q–Q7	 4	20 .... N–N3	....	....
21 P–QN4	... 3	21 .... R–Q1	....	....
22 Q–R4	 3	22 .... N–R5	....	....
23 P–B5	 3	23 .... NxN　*	....	....
24 P–B6	 7	24 .... PxP	....	....
25 PxP	 3	25 .... P–R3	....	....
26 P–N5	 4	26 .... P–R4	....	....
27 P–N6	 4	27 .... N–Q5	....	....
28 BxN	 3	28 .... PxB	....	....
29 QR–N1	... 4	29 .... P–Q4	....	....
30 P–K5	 4	30 .... Q–K3	....	....
31 Q–N5	 4	31 .... QxKP (e)	....	....
32 KR–K1	... 3	32 .... QxR†	....	....
33 RxQ		1	33 .... B–N5	....	....
34 QxQP	 5	34 .... Resigns	....	....

Total Score 100 | **Your Percentage _____**

SCALE: 75-100—Excellent; 55-74—Superior; 40-54—Good; 25-39—Fair

Notes on BLACKBURNE vs. JOHN

Blackburne flourished in the heyday of British chess. The quality of the English players then equaled in skill and surpassed in elegance that of the best Continental masters. Blackburne, Bird and Burn left a heritage of many immortal games.

Blackburne was the first master to practice simultaneous exhibitions, including blindfold séances, at one time playing simultaneously a half dozen games against strong amateurs without sight of board or men. (This record has been vastly surpassed in modern times by Alekhine, Koltanowski and Najdorf.) Blackburne is famous for announcing, blindfolded, a forced mate in sixteen moves, then rattling off the five different variations which constituted the combination.

In the present game he punishes John for his eccentric, time-losing Bishop moves. 24 P–B6, disdaining to recapture a piece, initiates the finale. A smart example of retribution against shoddy opening tactics.

NOTES TO THE GAME

* Position is diagrammed after 23 . . . NxN

a) An eccentric move which blocks the development of the Queen Bishop.

b) After 14 . . . B-Q2, White gains the outpost KB5 for his Knight with 15 B-N5.

c) But this move assures White of that outpost in any case.

d) A waste of time.

e) Else 32 PxP‡ leads to mate.

---

† = check; ‡ = double check; § = dis. check

A MAGIC SQUARE

WHAT is a square, more or less, between chess-players? With sixty-four on the board, there are surely enough. In the game, Reti–Moller, Gothenberg, 1920, one square is one too many! When White usurps KB5, the game is over. A Ruy Lopez, the game begins 1 P–K4, P–K4 2 N–KB3, N–QN3 3 B–N5.

Cover scoring table at line indicated. Set up position, make Black's next move (exposing table just enough to read it). Now guess White's 4th move, then expose it. Score par if your move agrees; zero, if not. Make move actually given, opponent's reply. Then guess White's next, and so on.

**COVER WHITE MOVES
IN TABLE BELOW.**   **EXPOSE ONE LINE AT A TIME**

White Played	Par Score	Black Played	Your Selection for White's move	Your Score
		3 .... B–B4	----------------	--------
4 O–O (a)	___3	4 .... KN–K2	----------------	--------
5 NxP!	_____4	5 .... NxN	----------------	--------
6 P–Q4	_____2	6 .... P–QB3	----------------	--------·
7 B–K2	_____3	7 .... B–Q3	----------------	--------·
8 PxN	_____2	8 .... BxP	----------------	--------
9 N–B3 (b)	__4	9 .... O–O	----------------	--------
10 P–B4	_____5	10 .... BxN	----------------	--------
11 PxB	_____2	11 .... P–Q4	----------------	--------
12 B–R3!	_____5	12 .... R–K1	----------------	--------
13 Q–Q4	_____4	13 .... Q–B2 ? (c)	----------------	--------
14 P–K5	_____5	14 .... B–B4	----------------	--------
15 B–Q3	_____3	15 .... Q–Q2	----------------	--------
16 P–R3	_____4	16 .... P–KR4 ? (d)	----------------	--------
17 Q–B2	_____3	17 .... N–N3 ?? (e)	----------------	--------
18 Q–B3	_____5	18 .... P–R5	----------------	--------
19 Q–R5	_____5	19 .... BxB	----------------	--------
20 PxB	_____2	20 .... P–Q5	----------------	--------
21 B–Q6!	_____6	21 .... PxP	----------------	--------
22 P–Q4	_____5	22 .... N–B1*	----------------	--------
23 P–B5	_____5	23 ... P–B3	----------------	--------
24 QR–B1	____5	24 ... N–R2	----------------	---.-----
25 RxP	_____3	25 .... Q–KB2	----------------	--------
26 QxP	_____3	26 .... QxP	----------------	--------
27 R–KN3	____3	27 .... K–R1	----------------	--------
28 R–B4	_____4	28 .... Q–N1	----------------	--------
29 PxP	_____3	29 .... R–K8† (f)	----------------	--------
30 K–R2	_____2	30 .... Resigns	----------------	--------

Total Score 100 | Your Percentage _____

SCALE: 75-100—Excellent; 55-74—Superior; 40-54—Good; 25-39—Fair

Notes on RETI vs. MOLLER

This game clearly shows the superiority of a "good" Bishop over a "bad" Knight. Black's downfall stems from loss of time finding some sanctuary for his horseman. While the Black cavalry retreat, the White foot soldiers infiltrate the Black King's hideaway.

Without so-called "material" gain, White's advantage in time and space, curtailing any counter-thrust on Black's part, assures the victory.

As early as 12 B–R3! Black is positionally bested. Reti shows with elegance and precision how to cash in tactically from a sound strategical motif.

It is pertinent to point out: The occupation of KB5 by a White piece or Pawn is the dominating theme of many King-side attacks.

* Position after 22 . . . N-B1

Notes to the Game

a) Not best. 4 P-B3, with 5 P-Q4 to follow, is stronger; score 4 for that choice.

b) Not 9 P-KB4 on account of 9 . . . Q-N3†, followed by . . . BxNP.

c) Here Black starts to go astray. 13 . . . N-B4! is the move.

d) An unnecessary weakening. 16 . . . P-QN3, with . . . P-B4 to come, is correct.

e) As an ultimate result of this move, Black loses his grip on his KB4 square!

f) The spite check.

---

†=check; ‡=double check; §=discovered check

NO COUNTING HOUSE FOR THIS KING

The old dogmatist Dr. Seigbert Tarrasch knew a thing or two about chess in his day, even though it was his misfortune from a point of view of ranking to live at the same time as Dr. Emanuel Lasker. Here, at Vienna 1922, he (White) takes Reti to task by exploiting a weak black square complex with, of all things, his King. The opening, a Caro-Kann, begins with 1 P–K4, P–QB3 2 N–QB3, P–Q4 3 N–B3, N–B3 4 PxP, PxP 5 P–Q4, B–N5 6 P–KR3, BxN 7 QxB, P–K3 8 B–Q3, N–B3 9 B–K3, B–K2 10 O–O.

Cover scoring table at line indicated. Set up position, make Black's next move (exposing table just enough to read it). Now *guess* White's 10th move, then expose it. Score par, if move agrees; zero, if not. Make move actually given, Black's reply. Then guess White's next, and so on.

COVER WHITE MOVES IN TABLE BELOW.

EXPOSE ONE LINE AT A TIME

White Played	Par Score	Black Played	Your Selection for White's move	Your Score
		10 . . . . O–O	. . . .	. . . .
11 P–QR3 2		11 . . . . P–QR3	. . . .	. . . .
12 N–K2 3		12 . . . . P–QN4	. . . .	. . . .
13 B–KB4 (a) 2		13 . . . . Q–N3	. . . .	. . . .
14 P–B3 2		14 . . . . N–QR4	. . . .	. . . .
15 QR–Q1 2		15 . . . . N–B5	. . . .	. . . .
16 B–B1 4		16 . . . . Q–B3	. . . .	. . . .
17 N–N3 4		17 . . . . P–QR4	. . . .	. . . .
18 KR–K1 4		18 . . . . P–N5	. . . .	. . . .
19 RPxP 2		19 . . . . PxP	. . . .	. . . .
20 N–B5! 5		20 . . . . PxN	. . . .	. . . .
21 RxB 2		21 . . . . PxP	. . . .	. . . .
22 PxP 2		22 . . . . P–N3 (b)	. . . .	. . . .
23 B–R6 5		23 . . . . N–N7	. . . .	. . . .
24 R–N1 2		24 . . . . NxB	. . . .	. . . .
25 QxN 2		25 . . . . KR–N1	. . . .	. . . .
26 RxR† 2		26 . . . . RxR	. . . .	. . . .
27 Q–N3 5		27 . . . . R–Q1	. . . .	. . . .
28 Q–K5 5		28 . . . . R–R1	. . . .	. . . .
29 R–B7 5		29 . . . . Q–K3 (c)	. . . .	. . . .
30 QxQ 5		30 . . . . PxQ	. . . .	. . . .
31 R–N7† 3		31 . . . . K–R1	. . . .	. . . .
32 R–K7 3		32 . . . . K–N1 (d)	. . . .	. . . .
33 P–B3 5		33 . . . . N–K1*	. . . .	. . . .
34 K–R2! (e) . 7		34 . . . . N–Q3	. . . .	. . . .
35 R–N7† 2		35 . . . . K–R1	. . . .	. . . .
36 R–Q7 2		36 . . . . N–N4	. . . .	. . . .
37 K–N3 3		37 . . . . NxBP	. . . .	. . . .
38 K–B4 3		38 . . . . N–N4	. . . .	. . . .
39 K–K5 3		39 . . . . R–K1	. . . .	. . . .
40 K–B6 4		40 . . . . Resigns (f)	. . . .	. . . .
Total Score 100		**Your Percentage**		

SCALE: 75-100—Excellent; 55-74—Superior; 40-54—Good; 25-39—Fair

Notes on TARRASCH vs. RETI

After White achieves the stranglehold with Rook on the seventh rank and Bishop at KR6 (acting as both vise and sword) he disdains the win of a Pawn which would allow Black to escape from the dungeon.

Note how helpless the freewheeling Knight is. He can find no way to stave off the White King's approach.

Strategically then, we may assert that as early as 22 . . . P–N3 Black is defeated. Again, thinking backward, undoubtedly Black's 6 . . . BxN was, to say the least, ill considered. This was too early a stage to allow the enemy the advantage of two Bishops.

A sharp example of the classic style of play on Tarrasch's part.

Position after 33 . . . N–K1

NOTES TO THE GAME

(a) To prevent the simplifying 13 . . . P–K4.

(b) Forced, to save the Bishop Pawn. But Black remains with a weakness on the black squares.

(c) The only move, and it leads to a losing endgame. Otherwise White has 30 Q–K7.

(d) 32 . . . N–N1 33 B–N7 mate.

(e) Key to the winning idea. White's King heads for KB7.

(f) If 40 . . . K–N1 41 R–N7†, K–R1 42 R–N7, N–Q3 43 R–Q7, N–N4 44 K–B7, R–KN1 45 R–Q8!!

† = check; ‡ = double check; § = dis. check